Other Titles of Interest

TEST EQUIPMENT
CONSTRUCTION

by

R. A. PENFOLD

**BERNARD BABANI (publishing) LTD
THE GRAMPIANS
SHEPHERDS BUSH ROAD
LONDON W6 7NF
ENGLAND**

Please Note

Although every care has been taken with the production of this book to ensure that any projects, designs, modifications and/or programs etc. contained herewith, operate in a correct and safe manner and also that any components specified are normally available in Great Britain, the Publishers do not accept responsibility in any way for the failure, including fault in design, of any project, design, modification or program to work correctly or to cause damage to any other equipment that it may be connected to or used in conjunction with, or in respect of any other damage or injury that may be so caused, nor do the Publishers accept responsibility in any way for the failure to obtain specified components.

Notice is also given that if equipment that is still under warranty is modified in any way or used or connected with home-built equipment then that warranty may be void.

© 1989 BERNARD BABANI (publishing) LTD

First Published — March 1989

British Library Cataloguing in Publication Data
Penfold, R. A.
    Test equipment construction.
    1. Electronic testing equipment.
      Construction ——— Amateurs
      manuals
    I. Title
      621.3815'48

    ISBN 0 85934 193 3

Printed and bound in Great Britain by Cox & Wyman Ltd, Reading

Preface

With modern electronics tending to become ever more complex, whether of the commercial or home constructed varieties, a good range of test equipment is an increasingly important part of the electronics enthusiasts' "armoury". A good multimeter has long been regarded as the most important item of test equipment, and it almost certainly remains so. An oscilloscope also remains an important acquisition for those who can afford one. However, these main items of test equipment can not deal with all eventualities, and are not appropriate for all situations. For example, few multimeters or oscilloscopes permit the testing of transistors or capacitors.

In this book some simple and inexpensive pieces of test equipment are described. They have been designed to fill in the gaps covered by most multimeters, and to cover the checking of both linear and digital circuits. Stripboard layouts are provided for all the designs, together with wiring diagrams where appropriate, plus notes on their construction and use. While the designs should prove useful for the more experienced readers, they are not beyond the capabilities of newcomers to the hobby. Apart from providing the constructor with a useful range of test gear, building these projects should also be an interesting and rewarding exercise in its own right.

R. A. Penfold

Warning

Never make tests on any mains powered equipment that is plugged into the mains unless you are quite sure you know exactly what you are doing.

Remember that capacitors can hold their charge for some considerable time even when equipment has been switched off and unplugged.

Contents

Chapter 1

AUDIO TEST GEAR

Whether you are interested in analogue or digital electronics, small or large projects, or a range of project types, the value of test equipment is something that should not be underestimated. In an ideal world there would be no need for test equipment at all. Projects would always work first time, and would continue to do so indefinitely. In the real world we are fallible, and do make mistakes when building projects. I constructed an embarrassingly large number of projects before one worked first time!

"Dud" components are very rare these days. The large numbers of dubious semiconductors that were once on sale as legitimate components seem to have disappeared from the market, or are sold as "untested" devices in bargain packs. Nevertheless, faulty components can still slip through testing procedures, or components that were originally serviceable can fail in use.

Mistakes in the component layout, short circuited tracks on a printed circuit board, and other faults of a largely mechanical nature can often be traced by a visual inspection of the circuit board etc. Some faults are not traceable in this way though, and tracking down a faulty component can be very difficult without the aid of suitable test gear. It can become a matter of replacing components in the hope that this substitution testing will bring to light the faulty component sooner rather than later!

AF Generator

A number of simple but useful test gear projects are described in this book, starting with some audio test equipment in this chapter. What could reasonably be regarded as the most essential piece of audio test gear is an audio signal generator. The unit described here has an operating frequency range of less than 20Hz to more than 20kHz in three ranges. These are 20Hz to 200Hz, 200Hz to 2kHz, and 2kHz to 20kHz. Each range is actually slightly wider than quoted above so that there

1

is a slight overlapping of ranges, and no risk of any gaps between them. Both sinewave and squarewave outputs signals are available, with an output level of about 2.8 volts peak to peak in both cases. In terms of r.m.s. voltage, this works out at about 1 volt r.m.s. for the sinewave signal. There is a volume control style variable attenuator plus a −20dB switched attenuator. The latter reduces the output voltage by a factor of ten, and makes it easier to accurately set a specific output level when low output voltages are required.

The sinewave output is the one that is used for most audio testing. The important attribute of a sinewave is that it contains only the fundamental frequency. Other repetitive waveforms contain harmonics (multiples of the fundamental frequency). With the squarewave output signal for example, there are strong odd order harmonics (i.e. three times, five times, seven times the fundamental frequency, etc.). Obviously for some types of testing, the purity of the output signal is not of great importance, and neither is the precise output frequency. In other cases they are both crucial, and this includes frequency response testing, which is one of the most common uses of audio signal generators. Squarewave test signals are mainly used in conjunction with an oscilloscope. Distortion of the wave shape can reveal irregularities in the frequency or phase response of a circuit, as well as other aspects of performance such as "ringing". Squarewave testing is a subject that we will return to later in this chapter.

Wien Bridge

For as long as I have been involved in electronics (about 25 years or so) the standard form of audio signal generator seems to have been a Wien Bridge type having thermistor stabilisation. The advantages of this form of oscillator are its excellent performance coupled with extreme simplicity. The only real drawback is that the thermistor to provide the gain stabilisation is relatively expensive, and is not the most widely available component. It is well worth the trouble and expense though. Oscillators using a good stabilising thermistor can easily provide distortion levels that are only a minute fraction of 1%, and maintain the output level to well within plus and minus 1dB over a very wide frequency range. A Wien Bridge oscillator with thermistor stabilisation might not be the latest thing in modern technology, but it still provides a level of performance that can not easily be bettered.

A Wien network consists of two resistors and two capacitors connected in the manner shown in Figure 1.1. It can be

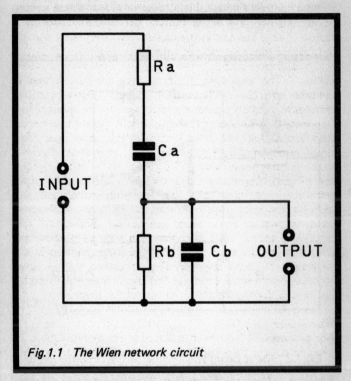

Fig. 1.1 The Wien network circuit

regarded as a phase shift network, and at a certain frequency the input and output will be in phase. For the mathematically minded, this frequency is obtained using this formula:

$$f = \frac{1}{2\pi CaRa}$$

It is assumed here that Ra = Rb, and that Ca = Cb, which is normally the case for a Wien network used in a real-world application. There is a loss of about 10dB (i.e. the output signal voltage is about one-third of the input signal level) at the zero phase shift frequency. In theory, all that is needed in order to produce a high quality sinewave oscillator is a setup of the type outlined in Figure 1.2. Here the Wien network is

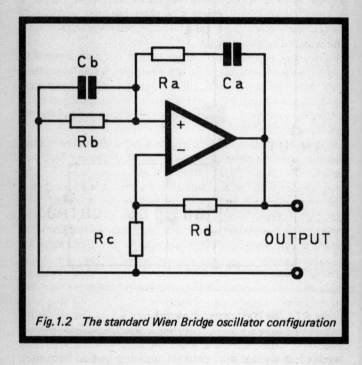

Fig.1.2   The standard Wien Bridge oscillator configuration

placed between the output and non-inverting input of an operational amplifier. It therefore provides positive feedback at the zero phase shift frequency, and provided the losses through the network are matched by the voltage gain through the amplifier, there will be sufficient feedback to sustain oscillation at this frequency.

In reality things are a little more tricky than this. Setting the voltage gain of the amplifier at three times by giving negative feedback resistors Rc and Rd the right values is not too difficult, but will not be satisfactory in practice. If the tolerances of these components should result in slightly too little gain the circuit will fail to oscillate. If their tolerances should result in marginally too much gain, excessively strong oscillation will result. This will cause the output signal to become clipped, and strong distortion products will result. In fact the output signal would be closer to a squarewave than the required sinewave signal!

One way around the problem is to use a gain control to permit manual adjustment of the oscillation level. In practice this does not work very well as changes in the frequency control, variations in the loading on the output, etc., make it necessary to almost continuously trim the gain control for the correct output level.

Some form of automatic gain control is much more satisfactory, and the most simple method is to replace feedback resistor Rd with a special form of thermistor. Most thermistors are designed to respond to the ambient temperature, but the type required for this application is the so-called "self heating" variety. These are contained in an evacuated glass envelope so that, as far as possible, they are isolated from the ambient temperature. The type used in this application are the usual negative temperature coefficient thermistors, which simply means that increased temperature gives reduced resistance. The temperature of the device is largely a function of the current which flows through it.

In this case the current flow depends on how strongly (or otherwise) the circuit is oscillating. Strong oscillation forces relatively large currents through the device, while with very weak oscillation there is virtually no current passed through it. Initially the thermistor is cold, it has a high resistance, and there is little negative feedback. This gives strong oscillation, as the voltage gain of the amplifier is inversely proportional to the amount of feedback. This oscillation forces relatively large currents through the thermistor, which consequently heats up and has greatly reduced resistance. This gives reduced voltage gain, and a lower output level. This in turn gives reduced current flow, higher gain, and greater output level. The output signal therefore wavers slightly at first, but it soon settles down at a steady compromise output level.

Provided the circuit is designed properly, this level will be one that produces low distortion. Also, any changes in loading or other factors that produce a change in the output level, unless they are of a really excessive nature, will be almost totally compensated for by the thermistor stabilisation. Whereas some other forms of gain control produce significant amounts of distortion, a thermistor provides what for most practical purposes can be regarded as pure resistance. Consequently its presence in the circuit does not result in any significant degradation of the distortion level.

Circuit Operation

Figure 1.3 shows the circuit diagram for the sinewave generator section of the unit. The squarewave signal is produced from

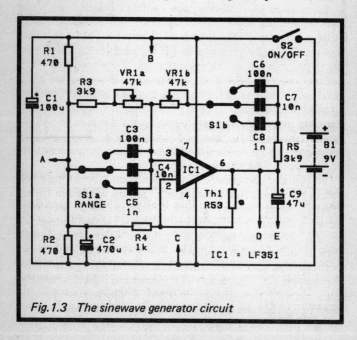

Fig.1.3 The sinewave generator circuit

the sinewave signal using a simple converter circuit which appears in Figure 1.4. This second diagram also includes the output attenuator circuit.

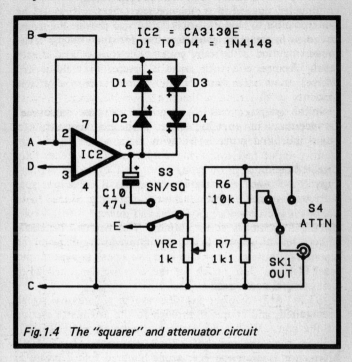

Fig.1.4 The "squarer" and attenuator circuit

The sinewave generator circuit follows the basic configuration of Figure 1.2 quite closely, but to permit operation with a single 9 volt battery (rather than the dual supplies required by standard operational amplifier configurations) R1, R2, and C2 are used to provide a centre tap on the supply lines. This is used for biasing purposes. Th1 is the stabilising thermistor. Three ranges are provided by having three sets of capacitors in the Wien network, with S1 being used to select the required set. If desired, a four way switch plus an extra pair of capacitors could be used to extend the coverage up to about 200kHz. The two extra capacitors would need to have a value of 100p in theory. However, due to stray circuit capacitances a value of 82p might offer better accuracy. A twin gang variable resistor (VR1) enables the output frequency to be continuously varied over the quoted ranges. It would be quite possible to have switched resistors to provide the ranges and a twin gang variable capacitor for fine tuning. The present method is the more popular one though, as it is very much cheaper, and each range is covered over about 270 degrees or so rather than the 180 degree travel of a variable capacitor.

In the squaring circuit IC2 operates as a voltage comparator. Its inverting input (pin 2) is biased to the central bias voltage, while the other input is fed with the sinewave signal. On positive input half cycles the output of IC2 switches fully high, while on negative going input half cycles it switches fully low. Ahtough I stated above that IC2's output goes fully positive and negative, this is not quite true. It tries to do so, but it is clamped at about plus and minus 1.3 to 1.4 volts by the four diodes at its output. This has two beneficial effects, one of which is to give an improved wave shape on the squarewave output. The other is to give a peak to peak output level that is a close match for the sinewave signal instead of being several times greater.

S3 is used to select the sinewave or squarewave signal, as required, and couple it through to the attenuator section of the unit. VR2 is the variable attenuator, while R6, R7, and S4 form the switched −20dB attenuator. If a −40dB attenuator is preferred (i.e. a one hundred fold decrease in the output level), simply change the value of R7 to 100 ohms.

The current consumption of the circuit is in the region of 15 to 16 milliamps, which is a little high to permit economic operation on a small 9 volt battery. A larger type such as six HP7 size cells in a plastic holder is a better choice.

Construction

Details of the stripboard layout for the audio signal generator project are shown in Figure 1.5. This requires a 0.1 inch pitch stripboard having 42 holes by 14 copper strips. Stripboard is

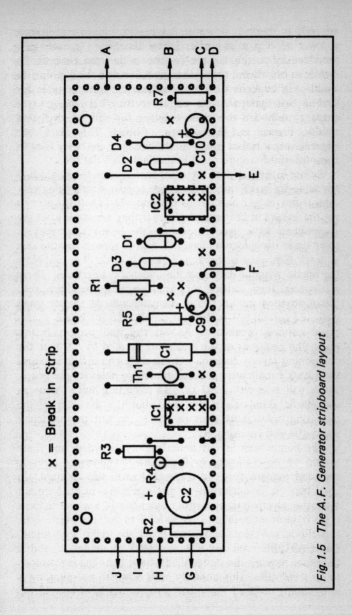

Fig. 1.5 The A.F. Generator stripboard layout

x = Break In Strip

9

not sold in this size, and a larger piece must be trimmed down to the correct size. A board of these dimensions is most easily produced by cutting a piece 14 strips wide from a standard 5 inch long board, and then trimming it down to the appropriate length. A hacksaw or junior hacksaw are both suitable for cutting this material. Do not try cutting between rows of strips as they are too close together for this to give good results. Instead, cut through rows of holes. This leaves sawn edges having a rather rough finish, but they are easily filed to a smooth finish using a small to medium sized flat file.

Before fitting any of the components onto the board it is advisable to make the breaks in the copper strips, being very careful not to get any out of position. In fact it is easier to get the breaks in the correct places if they are made after the components have been fitted onto the board. However, in some cases the soldered joints will tend to spread over the area of track that must be broken, making it difficult to complete the breaks without damaging the soldered connections. There is a special track cutting tool available, but a hand-held drill bit of about 4 millimetres in diameter will do the job quite well. Be careful not to cut too deeply into the board, as this could seriously weaken it. As with the other projects in this book, the positions of the breaks are marked by "X"s on the component layout diagram. At this stage you should also drill the two 3.2 millimetre diameter mounting holes for the board. These will take either M3 or 6BA mounting bolts. You can use plastic stand-offs if preferred, but the diameter of the mounting holes must then be chosen to suit the particular stand-offs you are using.

The component layout is not unduly crowded, and there should be no difficulty in fitting the components in place provided modern types of reasonably small size are used. In particular, it is advisable to use miniature printed circuit mounting electrolytic capacitors, apart from C1 where an axial type is more convenient. Be careful to get the electrolytic capacitors and semiconductors fitted the right way round. The CA3130E used for IC2 is a MOS input device, and it therefore requires the standard anti-static handling precautions to be observed. This basically boils down to not plugging it into circuit until all the other components have been fitted and all the wiring-up has been completed. Until that time it should be left in the protective packaging (such as a plastic tube or conductive foam) in which it should have been supplied. Use a holder for this component, and handle the device as little as possible when fitting it into the board. Although the LF351 used for IC1 is not a MOS input integrated circuit I would still recommend the use of a holder for this component (or any other d.i.l. integrated circuit come to that).

The thermistor (Th1) with its glass encapsulation should obviously be treated with reasonable respect. This component seems to be available as either an "RA53" or an "R53". As far as I can ascertain there is no difference between these two components, and either should work well in this circuit. No other types are likely to give good results though.

There are a few link wires needed, and trimmings from resistor and capacitor leadout wires will probably be sufficient for these. If not, some 22 or 24 s.w.g. tinned copper wire will be required. These link wires must be quite taut so that there is no risk of them short circuiting to any of the component leadout wires. Either this, or they must be fitted with p.v.c. sleeving to insulate them. At this stage only fit printed circuit pins to the board at the points where connections to off-board components will eventually be made. 1 millimetre diameter pins are required for normal 0.1 inch pitch stripboard.

It would probably be possible to fit this unit into quite a small case if required, but it will probably be easier to use if one having dimensions of about 150 by 100 by 50 millimetres or more is used. This avoids crowding of the controls on the front panel, and permits VR1 to be fitted with a fairly large calibrated scale if desired. A large scale is advantageous as it enables the output frequency to be set with greater accuracy. The exact layout of the front panel components is not critical, but the hard-wiring will be easier if the layout does not necessitate a large number of long trailing wires and crossed-over wires. I used a 3.5 millimetre jack socket for SK1, but any two way audio type should be suitable. Note that most 3.5 millimetre jack sockets are fitted with a break contact which is unused in this application. Hence one tag of this socket is left unconnected.

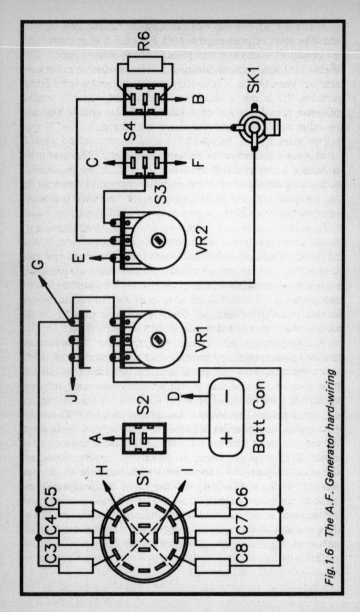

Fig. 1.6 The A.F. Generator hard-wiring

Figure 1.6 gives details of the hard-wiring, and this diagram must be used in conjunction with Figure 1.5 (e.g. point "A" in Figure 1.5 connects to point "A" in Figure 1.6). This wiring is largely straightforward, but some of the components are mounted on the switches, and the wiring will almost certainly be easier if these are added first. If the unit is powered from six HP7 size cells in a plastic holder, the connections to the holder are made via a standard PP3 type battery connector.

The capacitors in the Wien network (C3 to C8) are specified as having a tolerance of 5% or better in the components list. A fairly close tolerance for these components is important for two reasons. The first of these is simply that large tolerances could result in the frequency coverages of the three ranges being well away from the required ones. This could leave gaps in the coverage of the unit. The second reason is that it is much easier to calibrate the frequency control if a single scale is used for all three ranges. A single scale will only give good accuracy on all three ranges if the sets of capacitors have a close tolerance, so that there is an accurate ratio of ten to one between one range and the next. I would regard 5% as the minimum acceptable tolerance, and 1% or 2% is better.

The two attenuator resistors are specified as 2% types, and this is to ensure a reasonably accurate reduction by 20dB when the attenuated output is selected. However, you should bear in mind that loading on the output of the unit will have some effect on the output level, especially when the unit is set for anything other than maximum output. The exact effect of output loading depends on the input impedance of the circuit driven by the unit. With a high input impedance of about 100k or more there is unlikely to be any significant reduction in the output level. With a load impedance of a few tens of ohms or less the unit may well be overloaded and cease to function properly at all. Where precise output levels are required it is essential to monitor the output level using an a.c. millivoltmeter or an oscilloscope, rather than relying on any calibration on the attenuator controls.

Components for Figures 1.3 and 1.4

Resistors (all 0.25 watt 5% unless noted)
R1	470
R2	470
R3	3k9
R4	1k
R5	3k9
R6	10k (2% tolerance)
R7	1k1 (2% tolerance)

Potentiometers
VR1	47k 1in dual gang (see text)
VR2	1k 1in

Capacitors
C1	100μ 10V axial elect
C2	470μ 10V radial elect
C3	100n plastic foil 5% or better
C4	10n plastic foil 5% or better
C5	1n plastic foil 5% or better
C6	100n plastic foil 5% or better
C7	10n plastic foil 5% or better
C8	1n plastic foil 5% or better
C9	47μ 16V radial elect
C10	47μ 16V radial elect

Semiconductors
IC1	LF351
IC2	CA3130E
D1	1N4148
D2	1N4148
D3	1N4148
D4	1N4148

Miscellaneous
SK1	3.5mm jack socket
S1	3 way 4 pole rotary (only two poles used)
S2	SPST miniature toggle
S3	SPDT miniature toggle

S4   SPST miniature toggle
B1   9 volt (e.g. 6 x HP7 cells in plastic holder)
Th1   R53 or RA53 thermistor
Case
0.1 inch matrix stripboard 14 strips by 42 holes
Two control knobs
Two 8 pin DIL IC holders
Battery connector
Wire, solder, 6BA or M3 fixings, etc.

Testing and Calibration

In order to check the unit it is obviously necessary to have some means of monitoring of its output signal. Ideally an oscilloscope should be used, but an audio amplifier and a loudspeaker will suffice. Medium or high impedance headphones are also suitable, as is a crystal earphone. It is just a matter of checking that an output signal is present, that the attenuator controls enable the output level to be adjusted, and that the frequency controls provide coverage of the full audio range. Bear in mind that the sinewave output from the unit will be inaudible at the extremes of the frequency range. Accordingly, the fact that no output is audible at very high and very low frequencies does not necessarily mean that the unit is faulty. In all probability it is not. You can check that the unit is functioning at very low frequencies by switching to the squarewave mode. The harmonics on this signal should be clearly audible even if the fundamental frequency is not. A lack of any clearly audible output with the controls set for a low frequency sinewave, but a low frequency "buzzing" sound when the unit is set for squarewave operation, is a good indication that the unit is functioning correctly. If no output can be detected regardless of the control settings, or there is obvious distortion on the sinewave output, switch off at once and recheck all the wiring.

For the generator to be really useful it is essential for it to be fitted with an accurate frequency scale around VR1's control knob. If some form of frequency meter or an accurately calibrated oscilloscope is available there should be no difficulty in providing the unit with a suitable scale. Without the aid of suitable test equipment things are very much more difficult. About the only other option is to use a musical instrument to provide a range of known frequencies. The signal generator can then be tuned to the same pitches "by ear". This is a list of frequencies from middle A to the A one octave higher.

A	440Hz
A#	466Hz
B	494Hz
C	523Hz
C#	554Hz
D	587Hz
D#	622Hz
E	659Hz
F	698Hz
F#	740Hz
G	784Hz
G#	831Hz
A	880Hz

In each case these frequencies have been rounded up or down to the nearest Hertz. At frequencies of a few hundred Hertz you are unlikely to be able to produce a scale that can be read to within 1Hz. In fact the calibration points will probably have to be quite well spread out, but this should still provide a frequency scale that is adequate for most audio testing. Although only a limited range of frequencies are covered by the notes given above, bear in mind that an increase by one octave represents a doubling of frequency, while a reduction by one octave represents a halving in frequency. The note of B is a useful one as it is very close to 500Hz. Therefore, the Bs one octave above and below this are at frequencies close to 1kHz and 250Hz respectively. Obviously a musical instrument which has a wide compass will provide a good range of calibration frequencies.

A point to note is that the scaling is far from linear. The scale is well spread out at the low frequency end of the range but is much more cramped at the high frequency end. It is possible to obtain something close to linear scaling by using a potentiometer having an anti-log law for VR1. However, a suitable component is likely to prove impossible to obtain. An alternative is to use a log law potentiometer, but reverse connected (i.e. swop over the two track connections for each gang). The only disadvantage of this system is that the scale is reverse reading, with clockwise adjustment of VR1 producing a decrease in frequency.

An audio signal generator can be used in isolation as a signal injector, but it is normally operated in conjunction with other test equipment such as an audio millivoltmeter. We will consider the use of an audio signal generator for such tests as frequency response and voltage gain testing later in this chapter.

Squarewave Testing

If you have access to an oscilloscope, this can reveal some basic information about the phase and frequency response of a circuit when used in conjunction with the squarewave output of the signal generator. The basic technique is to simply inject the squarewave signal into the circuit under test, choosing sensible amplitude and frequency settings, and to then view the resultant output waveform. If the signal undergoes no significant changes in phase or frequency content it should emerge unaltered, as in Figure 1.7(a).

With an ideal squarewave signal the waveform jumps instantly from one level to the other. No practical circuit can produce such a waveform, but with most audio squarewave generators the rise and fall times of the circuit are no more than about a microsecond. Any lack of frequency response in a circuit that passes a squarewave will result in an increase in the rise and fall times. Figure 1.7(b) shows the effect of both inadequate high frequency bandwidth and phase shifting (which usually accompany any high frequency roll-off). Figure 1.7(c), shows the waveform obtained with the high frequency roll-off but no attendant phase shifting.

Inadequate low frequency response results in the horizontal parts of the waveform sloping diagonally, and a rise in the frequency response above the squarewave frequency has a similar effect. Figure 1.7(d) shows the effect of this rising response, while Figure 1.7(e) shows the effect of low frequency roll-off. A rising low frequency response gives rounded tops

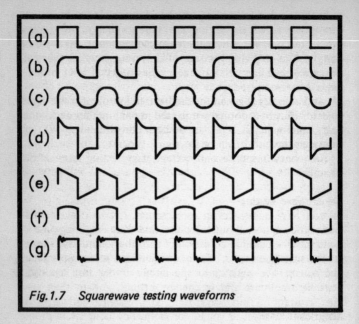

Fig.1.7 Squarewave testing waveforms

and bottoms to the waveform, as in Figure 1.7(f).

Instability can manifest itself in a number of similar ways. In a mild case there would be slight over-shoot on the leading and trailing edges of each cycle. In a more extreme case there would be "ringing", as in Figure 1.7(g).

These waveforms are all dependent on a suitable input frequency being chosen. When testing tone controls of an amplifier for example, a middle audio frequency of about 800Hz to 1kHz would be selected. Adjusting the tone controls should then have the appropriate effect on the output waveform. Obviously this system does not provide precise information about phase and frequency responses, but it is useful for giving certain types of equipment a quick check.

Test Bench Amplifier
A test bench amplifier is one of those simple little gadgets that no one involved with audio equipment can afford to

be without. It can be used for checking signal sources such as microphones, tuners, tape decks, etc., as well as operating as a signal tracer when checking faulty equipment. Basically a unit of this type is just an audio power amplifier having reasonably good sensitivity and a high input impedance. This permits low output devices such as microphones to be checked, and ensures minimal loading on any audio circuit being tested. High output power is not usually of prime importance, and a small battery powered device is adequate for most purposes.

This bench amplifier requires an input of only about 10 millivolts r.m.s. for maximum output, but it will produce a clearly audible output from inputs of below 1 millivolt r.m.s. The output power is less than 100 milliwatts into the built-in high impedance loudspeaker, but this provides reasonable volume (aided by the fact that high impedance loudspeakers tend to be somewhat more efficient than lower impedance types of a similar size). The input impedance depends on the setting of the volume control, but is always quite high at around 200 to 500 kilohms.

Amplifier Circuit

The full circuit diagram for the Test Bench Amplifier appears in Figure 1.8. It is a two stage affair having TR1 as the preamplifier and IC1 as the class B power amplifier.

The preamplifier is a common emitter amplifier. A stage of this type would normally be expected to have a very high level of voltage gain (often in excess of 40dB). In this case the voltage gain is quite modest at about 20dB (ten times) due to the local negative feedback provided by unbypassed emitter resistor R3. Slightly higher voltage gain would be quite useful, but a realistic figure for the overall voltage gain must be selected. A very high level of voltage gain runs the risk of instability due to stray feedback. There are also problems with stray pick-up of electrical noise such as mains "hum" when the input of the unit is left open circuit, or when it is fed from a high source impedance. The level of gain obtained with the specified value for R3 provides useful results without too much risk of problems with instability or excessive stray pick-up.

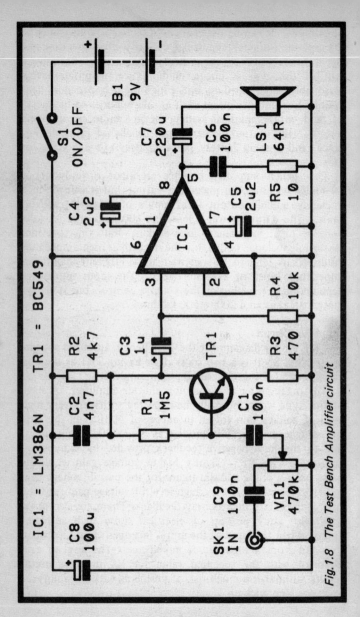

Fig.1.8 The Test Bench Amplifier circuit

20

A useful byproduct of the negative feedback provided by R3 is that it boosts the input impedance of TR1, thus avoiding the need for a separate input buffer stage. The input impedance is shunted somewhat by the volume control, VR1. This must be included at the input of the circuit as the input level could be quite high in some instances. Although there are advantages in having the volume control between the preamplifier and power amplifier stages, this is not an acceptable way of arranging things in this application, since there would be a strong likelihood of the input stage being severely overloaded on many occasions. C2 provides a small amount of high frequency roll-off, and this aids good stability.

Capacitor C9 was not included in the original design, but was added to the final version. Without this component there are two problems that can occur. The first of these is that there may be a d.c. component on the input signal. Without C9 included in the circuit this d.c. signal will be present across VR1's track and will tend to make operation of this control rather "noisy". It could even result in the biasing of the circuit being temporarily shifted to unusable levels each time VR1 was adjusted. The second reason is simply that the resistance of VR1 could shunt bias components in the circuit under test. This could cause a malfunction in the circuit under investigation each time the amplifier was connected to it. This could obviously cause confusing and misleading results.

The audio power amplifier device is the LM386N, which is a fairly standard low power type. Using a 9 volt supply it is capable of delivering a few hundred milliwatts r.m.s. into an 8 ohm impedance loudspeaker. The use of a high impedance loudspeaker and the lower output power that this provides is probably advisable in this case though. Using a low impedance loudspeaker the component layout and wiring needs to be carefully designed and implemented if problems with earth loops are to be avoided. Construction is far less critical using a high impedance loudspeaker, the battery consumption is much lower, and the volume is still quite adequate.

C6 and R5 form a "Zobel" network at the output, and this helps to avoid problems with instability caused by anomalies in the loudspeaker's impedance characteristic. C5 is a decoupling capacitor, and C4 is part of the negative feedback network which sets the voltage gain of IC1. The other feedback components are included within IC1. The typical closed loop voltage gain is 26dB (twenty times).

The quiescent current consumption of the circuit is only about 5 milliamps, but it is several times higher than this on volume peaks. A PP3 size 9 volt battery is adequate as the power source, but if the unit is likely to receive a great deal of use it is probably better to use a higher capacity battery. Six HP7 size cells in a plastic holder should suffice. The connection to this type of holder is made via a standard PP3 style battery clip.

Construction

The stripboard layout for the Test Bench Amplifier project is shown in Figure 1.9. It requires a board having 32 holes by 16 copper strips.

I will not give a detailed description of building the board as the method used is much the same as for the Audio Signal Generator project described earlier in this chapter. IC1 is not a MOS input device, but I would still recommend the use of a holder for this component.

It should be possible to fit the unit into any medium sized plastic box (i.e. one about 150 by 100 by 50 millimetres). A loudspeaker grille is required, and my preferred method of producing one of these is to simply drill a matrix of small holes (say about 5 millimetres in diameter). Take due care when drilling the holes as it is very easy to get some of them just slightly out of position, and this can give the finished unit a rather scrappy appearance. An alternative method is to make a large cutout in the front panel and to then glue some loudspeaker material in place behind this. Plastic grille material is also suitable, but seems to be difficult to obtain these days.

Built-in mounting brackets are a standard feature on medium and large loudspeakers, but seem to be absent from virtually all miniature types. This leaves little option but to glue the loudspeaker in position behind the grille. Any good quality general purpose adhesive should be suitable. I mostly use a quick setting epoxy type for this sort of thing. Be

22

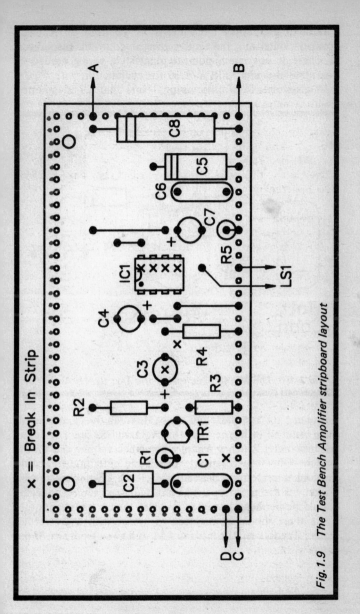

x = Break In Strip

Fig. 1.9   The Test Bench Amplifier stripboard layout

23

careful to only apply the adhesive to the front of the loud-speaker's outer rim, and avoid getting any onto the diaphragm.

There is not much point-to-point style wiring needed to complete the unit. Figure 1.10 (in conjunction with Figure 1.9) gives details of this wiring. Note that C9 is mounted

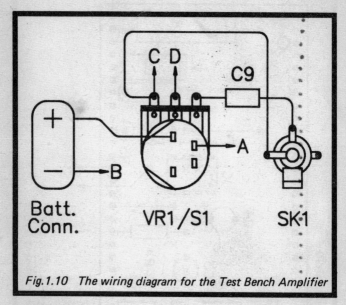

Fig.1.10 The wiring diagram for the Test Bench Amplifier

between VR1 and SK1, and is not fitted on the circuit board. It is assumed in Figure 1.10 that VR1 and S1 are a switched potentiometer which provides a combined volume and on/off switch. Obviously a separate switch and potentiometer could be used if preferred. Similarly, SK1 is a 3.5 millimetre jack socket on the prototype, but any two way audio connector should be perfectly suitable. Provided the wiring is kept quite short there should be no need to bother with any screened leads. Try to keep the leads to LS1 well away from any of the input wiring.

Components for Figure 1.8

Resistors (all 0.25 watt 5%)
R1	1M5
R2	4k7
R3	470
R4	10k
R5	10

Potentiometer
| VR1 | 470k log with switch (S1) |

Capacitors
C1	100n polyester
C2	4n7 polystyrene
C3	1μ 63V radial elect
C4	$2\mu2$ 63V radial elect
C5	$2\mu2$ 63V axial elect
C6	100n polyester
C7	200μ 10V radial elect
C8	100μ 10V axial elect
C9	100n polyester

Semiconductors
| IC1 | LM386N |
| TR1 | BC549 |

Miscellaneous
S1	Part of VR1
SK1	3.5mm jack socket
B1	9 volt (e.g. 6 x HP7 size cells in holder)
LS1	66mm diameter, 64R impedance

Case about 150 x 100 x 50mm
0.1 inch pitch stripboard 32 holes by 16 copper strips
Battery connector
8 pin d.i.l. holder
Control knob
Fixings, wire, solder, etc.

In Use

You could use ordinary multimeter type test prods with a unit of this kind, but this is not a particularly good way of doing things. The problem is that there tends to be strong pick-up of electrical noise by the long and unscreened (non-earthy) input lead. A better method for an application of this type is to use a screened lead to connect the test prods to SK1. On the face of it this leaves the user with two test prods very close together, and probably unusable in many situations. In practice the earthy test prod is usually connected to the outer braiding of the screened cable via a fairly long insulated lead (ordinary multistand connecting wire is suitable for this). This gives good separation of the test prods, but keeps the non-earthy lead screened as far as possible. Figure 1.11 illustrates this general scheme of things.

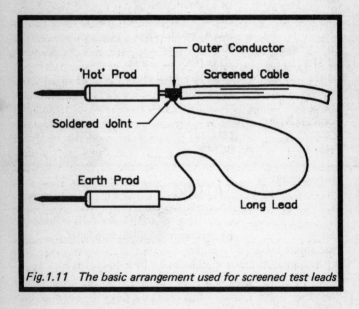

Fig.1.11 *The basic arrangement used for screened test leads*

Make sure you connect the screened cable to the 3.5 millimetre jack plug correctly. The small tag towards the front of the plug is the non-earthy ("hot") one, and the larger tag (which is usually part of the cable grip) is the earth tag.

In use it is just a matter of switching on using S1, connecting the input signal to the unit, and adjusting VR1 for a suitable volume level. If you use the unit as a signal tracer it is important to ensure that the unit under test is fed with a suitable test signal for you to trace! The normal input signal of the equipment is probably the best one to use wherever possible, as this will obviously be at the correct amplitude. If this is not practical for some reason, then a unit such as the Audio Signal Generator project described earlier should be able to provide a suitable test signal. If you use a signal generator as the signal source, set it to the sinewave mode. Any distortion will be readily detectable by ear using a sinewave test signal.

There are several techniques for fault-finding with the aid of a signal tracer, although these are really just variations on the fundamental method of operation. It is basically a matter of checking for a suitable signal level at various points in the circuit under test. In some cases it is not a lack of signal that is the problem, but severe distortion. In this eventuality you check for a distorted signal rather than a lack of signal level.

What you are searching for are two points in the circuit that are close together; one which provides a suitable signal and one that does not. The fault is then at or very close to the point in the circuit where there is a lack of signal or excessive distortion. It is important to realise that signal tracing techniques do not always narrow down the fault to a specific component. In most cases only the general area of the fault is identified. Some further testing, such as voltage and component checks, will then usually identify exactly which component or components are faulty.

As an example of how signal tracing is undertaken, assume that the test bench amplifier is to be used for signal tracing on another test bench amplifier unit of the same design. Some form of audio signal would be connected to the input of the amplifier under test, and this could be (say) the audio output from the earphone socket of a transistor radio, or the output of an audio signal generator. The first check could be at SK1 to test that the input signal was getting through to the socket correctly. A lot of faults with audio equipment actually turn

27

out to be problems with faulty plugs and leads! The next test points could be at the top end of VR1's track and at its wiper. The signal should be much the same at the top of VR1's track as it was at SK1, but at the wiper it should be possible to vary the signal level by altering VR1's setting. The next test would be at the base of TR1, where the signal level should be much the same as at the wiper of VR1. Bear in mind that at any point in the circuit after the volume control, the signal level will vary according to the setting of the volume control.

TR1's collector is the next test point, and as TR1 provides about 20dB of voltage gain, the signal level here should be noticeably higher than that at TR1's base. You can not make precise gain measurements using a test bench amplifier, but with experience you can learn to gauge voltage gains reasonably accurately.

It can sometimes be helpful to test for signals at places other than in the main signal path. In this case there is no bypass capacitor across R3, and the signal level here should be very much the same as that at the base of TR1. With a lot of common emitter amplifiers that have an emitter resistor it is bypassed by a capacitor, and there should then be no significant signal level at the emitter of the transistor. If a significant signal level is detected, this would suggest that the bypass capacitor is faulty. In a similar vein, it can sometimes be helpful to test for a signal on the non-earthy supply rail. This often has a supply decoupling capacitor (like C8), and in a fairly complex audio circuit there will normally be one or more R − C filter stages in the supply to the early stages of the circuit. There would normally be little or no detectable signal on the supply rails, and the presence of a significant signal level would strongly suggest that one of the supply decoupling capacitors was faulty.

For the sake of this example we will assume that the signal is found to be present and correct at the collector of TR1, but is absent at pin 3 of IC1. The fault obviously lies in the circuitry around C3, but it is not necessarily C3 that is faulty. As the signal is present at TR1's collector it would seem unlikely that the fault lies on this side of C3. Although not necessarily due to C3 being faulty, with further thought it would seem quite likely that this component is indeed the

28

cause of the problem. However, R4 having gone closed circuit could give the same result. On the other hand, this would place strong loading on the output of TR1, and would almost certainly produce quite noticeable distortion on the output from TR1 except at very low signal levels. A fault at the input of IC1 could have a similar effect. In the absence of any strong distortion on the output from TR1 it would seem likely that C3 is the faulty component, or that it is not connected into circuit properly. A few continuity checks, component checks, or component substitutions should sort out the precise nature of the problem.

Audio Millivoltmeter

A test bench amplifier is all that is needed for much audio testing, but its inability to measure precise signal levels is a severe handicap for many types of checking. For tests such as accurate gain measurements and frequency response testing it is essential to have a device that can at least accurately measure relative signal levels. Ideally it should also be able to measure absolute a.c. voltages with reasonable accuracy. One method of measuring signal levels is to use an oscilloscope. Although these instruments often seem to be regarded as only for viewing waveforms, they are in fact used just as much for voltage and time measurements as for viewing wave shapes. Despite price drops in "real terms" over the years, an oscilloscope is still a fairly expensive item of equipment, and one which a lot of amateur electronics enthusiasts consider (quite understandably) to be far too expensive to be worth buying.

A cheaper alternative for audio signal measurements is an a.c. millivoltmeter. This is similar to an ordinary multimeter switched to an a.c. voltage range. However, whereas most multimeters have a full scale value of a few volts on their most sensitive a.c. voltage range, an a.c. millivoltmeter at its most sensitive might require only a millivolt or less for full scale deflection of the meter. Also, it has a relatively high input impedance so that readings are not affected by substantial loading on the circuit under test. Another difference is that many multimeters switched to an a.c. voltage range offer a bandwidth that is somewhat less than the full audio range. Digital instruments tend to be the worst offenders in this respect, and often have an upper limit to their frequency responses of only a few hundred hertz. Most a.c. millivoltmeters have upper frequency responses that extend well beyond the upper limit of the audio range, often to frequencies of a few hundred kilohertz or more.

This is a relatively simple instrument that offers three measuring ranges with full scale values of 10 millivolts r.m.s., 100 millivolts r.m.s., and 1 volt r.m.s. The input impedance is over 1 megohm, although the unavoidable input capacitance reduces the input impedance significantly at high frequencies. On all three ranges the upper limit of the frequency response is beyond the 20kHz upper limit of the audio frequency range, but due to the simplicity of the design the response does not extend far beyond 20kHz. This offers adequate performance for most audio testing, while not providing such high levels of sensitivity, bandwidth, and input impedance that the unit becomes excessively difficult to build and use.

Linearity

On the face of it there is no difficulty in producing an a.c. millivoltmeter that will provide accurate results. All that is needed is an amplifier driving a meter via a rectifier circuit. In reality a circuit of this type is unlikely to give really good results. The problem is the severe non-linearity of semiconductor diodes. Silicon types are amongst the worst offenders, and these require a forward voltage of around 0.5 to 0.6 volts before they will start to conduct significantly. There are diodes which perform better in this respect, including the old germanium and gold bonded types (the latter being a popular choice for a.c. meter circuits).

Even using these lower voltage drop diodes, at low input voltages there is usually quite significant non-linearity. In analogue multimeters the normal way around the problem is to use a separate scale for the lower a.c. voltage ranges, with the scale being adjusted to match the non-linearity of the diodes. This is not a very convenient way of tackling the problem in a home constructor project where accurately calibrating the finished unit could prove to be very difficult. Ideally what is needed is a circuit that provides linear scaling so that the original scale of the meter can be utilized.

This can be achieved by using negative feedback to compensate for the non-linearity of the diodes. Even using diodes with a large forward voltage drop it is possible to obtain really good linearity if sufficient feedback is used (although results will always be that much better using low voltage drop diodes). Figure 1.12 shows the standard method of using negative feedback to overcome the non-linearity of semiconductor diodes.

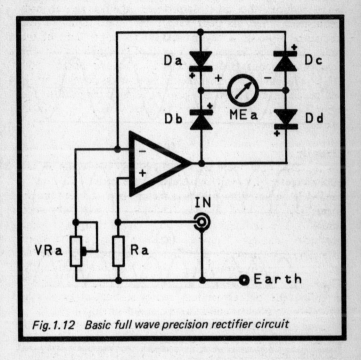

Fig. 1.12 Basic full wave precision rectifier circuit

The circuit is basically a standard operational amplifier non-inverting mode circuit. However, rather than driving the rectifier and meter from the output of the amplifier and the 0 volt earth rail, they are included as part of the negative feedback circuit. With insufficient output voltage to drive the diodes into conduction, there is no significant feedback and

31

the amplifier exhibits its full open loop voltage gain. Thus, only a very small input voltage is needed in order to produce a large output voltage. What happens in practice is that very early in each input half cycle the output voltage becomes sufficiently large to bring the diodes into conduction. Strong negative feedback is then applied to the amplifier, which consequently has a much lower closed loop voltage gain. A sinewave input signal, as in Figure 1.13(a), therefore provides a rectified output signal more like that of Figure 1.13(b).

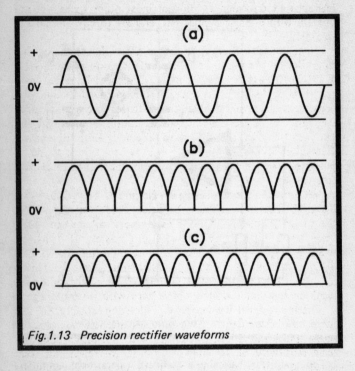

Fig. 1.13 Precision rectifier waveforms

Due to the voltage drops through the diodes, this gives a properly rectified signal across the meter, as in Figure 1.13(c). The feedback is effectively boosting the output voltage by an amount which is equal to the voltage drop through the diodes, and which consequently compensates for this voltage loss.

The Circuit

Figure 1.14 shows the full circuit diagram of the a.c. millivolt-meter project, and as will be apparent from this, the unit is based on just a single integrated circuit. This is the CA3130E, which is a high performance operational amplifier that can provide excellent bandwidth, a very high input impedance, and will operate with a single supply rail. The use of other operational amplifiers in this circuit is not recommended, and would almost certainly result in grossly inadequate performance. In fact most other types will not operate with a single supply rail, and are totally unusable in this circuit.

This circuit uses a form of rectifier that is somewhat simplified in comparison to the configuration of Figure 1.12. It differs from this mainly in that it is based on a half wave rectifier, not a full wave type. D1 is included in the feed-back circuit in order to compensate for the voltage drop through D2, and the method of operation is essentially the same as that of the full wave circuit. Both diodes are germanium types so that IC1 has as little work to do as possible. This helps to maintain good performance at high frequencies.

VR2 enables the sensitivity of the unit to be varied so that it can be accurately calibrated. In the "BATT" position of S2 the meter is used to monitor the battery voltage, and ME1 then has a full scale reading of approximately 10 volts. A reading of less than about 7.5 volts indicates that a new battery is required. VR1 is an offset null control. This is used to trim out any offset voltages that might otherwise result in the meter reading above zero with no input signal.

The input signal is taken via d.c. blocking capacitor C2 to a three step attenuator. This provides attenuation levels of 0dB, 20dB, and 40dB. Together with the unit's basic full scale sensitivity of 10 millivolts r.m.s., this gives full scale sensitivities of 10 millivolts r.m.s on range 1, 100 millivolts r.m.s. on range 2, and 1 volt r.m.s. on range 3. As the attenuator is in a high impedance part of the circuit there is a risk of it introducing anomalies in the frequency response of the unit. In practice this does not seem to be a major prob-lem, especially as the unit is not intended for operation at

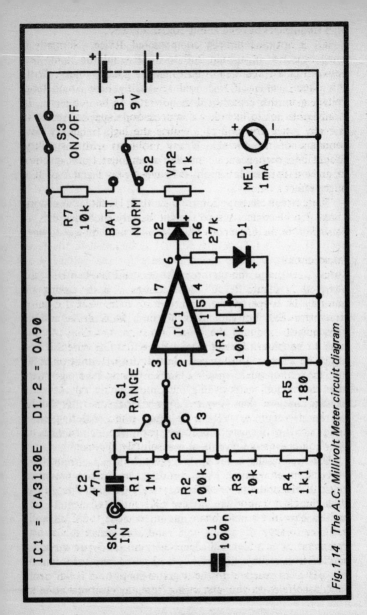

Fig. 1.14   The A.C. Millivolt Meter circuit diagram

IC1 = CA3130E   D1, 2 = OA90

high frequencies beyond about 20kHz anyway.

IC1 is not an internally compensated device. Normally a small capacitor of around 2pF to 30pF would be connected between pins 1 and 8 in order to ensure good stability. With this circuit, where IC1 is used at a fairly high closed loop voltage gain, this capacitor does not seem to be necessary. It is advisable not to include a compensation capacitor unless it is really necessary as it will reduce the high frequency performance of the circuit. If any problems with instability should be experienced, connecting a compensation capacitor of around 1pF or 2pF in value between pins 1 and 8 of IC1 might effect a cure.

The current consumption of the circuit is quite low at only about 2 milliamps. A small 9 volt battery such as a PP3 or equivalent is therefore perfectly adequate as the power source.

Construction
Details of the stripboard for the a.c. millivolt meter are provided in Figure 1.15. This requires a board having 17 holes by 19 copper strips. Construction of the board is quite straightforward, but note that IC1 is a MOS device which consequently requires the usual anti-static handling precautions to be taken. Do not overlook the four link wires. If the preset resistors are to fit into the layout properly they must be miniature horizontal mounting types. D1 and D2 are germanium diodes, and as such they are more vulnerable to heat damage than are the more common silicon types. It should not be necessary to use a heat shunt when soldering these components into place, but do not apply the iron to each of these joints for any longer than is absolutely necessary.

The hard-wiring is shown in Figure 1.16. It is important that the input wiring is kept as short as possible to minimise any risk of instability or excessive stray pick up in this wiring. It is therefore important to have SK1 mounted near to S1, and to have the circuit board mounted close to S1 as well. Also try to keep the wiring to S2 and ME1 reasonably short, and as far as possible, well separated from the input wiring. I would strongly urge the use of an all metal case for this project. If this is earthed to the negative supply rail it will tend to shield the sensitive input wiring from any electrical noise in

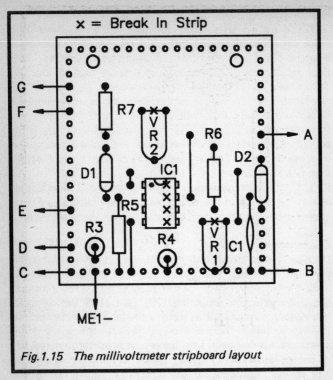

x = Break In Strip

Fig.1.15 The millivoltmeter stripboard layout

the vicinity of the unit. If an ordinary 3.5 millimetre jack socket is used for SK1, this will provide the earth connection to the case. If an insulated socket of some kind is used for SK1, then a soldertag on the case can be used to provide an earth connection point.

S1 is a standard 3 way 4 pole rotary switch, but in this application only one pole is required. This leaves nine of its tags unused. R1 and R2 are mounted on S1, and C2 is mounted between S1 and SK1. This helps to minimise the amount of input wiring and aids good stability. It is obviously helpful if C2 is a type which has fairly long leadout wires, rather than one which has very short leads for printed circuit mounting. However, if necessary it should not be too hard to solder short extension leads to C2. Note that the attenuator resistors (R1

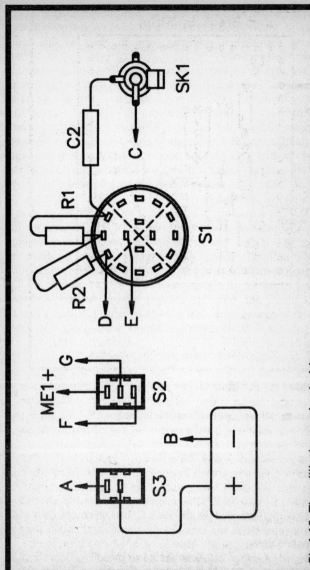

Fig. 1.16 The millivoltmeter hard-wiring

37

to R4) should have a tolerance of 2% (and preferably 1%) in order to ensure good accuracy on all three ranges. Avoid overheating them when soldering them in place, as this could impair their accuracy.

One slightly awkward aspect of construction is mounting the meter. These mostly require quite a large circular cutout, usually about 38 millimetres in diameter. Without access to sophisticated cutting equipment, a fret or coping saw represents about the easiest method of making this cutout. A miniature round file can also be used, but will make somewhat tougher going of the task. Either way, it is probably best to cut just inside the line marking the perimeter of the cutout. Then use a large round file to enlarge the cutout to precisely the required size.

Any recalibration of the meter is not really necessary. The 0−1 scale is correct for the 1 volt range, and on the other two ranges it is not difficult to convert meter readings to the millivolt readings they represent. If you do decide to add to the meter's scale, proceed with great caution. It is quite easy to take off the front panel of most meters, unscrew the scale plate, add some figures using rub-on transfers, and then reassemble everything. On the other hand, it is even easier to damage the delicate meter mechanism while doing this. You have been warned!

Components for Figure 1.14

Resistors (all 0.25 watt 5% unless noted)
R1	1M 2%
R2	100k 2%
R3	10k 2%
R4	1k1 2%
R5	180
R6	27k
R7	10k 2%

Potentiometers
VR1	100k sub-min hor preset
VR2	1k sub-min hor preset

Capacitors
C1   100n ceramic
C2   47n polyester

Semiconductors
IC1   CA3130E
D1   OA90
D2   OA90

Miscellaneous
ME1   1mA moving coil panel meter
S1   3 way 4 pole rotary (only 1 pole used)
S2   SPDT miniature toggle
S3   SPST miniature toggle
B1   9 volt (PP3 size)
SK1   3.5mm jack socket
Metal instrument case
Battery connector
Control knob
0.1 inch pitch stripboard 17 holes by 19 strips
Pins, fixings, wire, solder, etc.

Calibration

Obviously the unit must be accurately calibrated if it is to be
used for absolute measurements. For relative tests such as
frequency response measurements a lack of calibration accuracy will not hinder results. In order to calibrate the unit you
will require a sinewave signal source (such as the audio signal
generator unit described previously) and an a.c. voltmeter,
oscilloscope, or millivoltmeter. It is unlikely that many constructors of this project will have access to either an oscilloscope or a.c. millivoltmeter, but presumably anyone building
the unit will have a multimeter in their possession.

Digital multimeters probably offer the best alternative to an
a.c. voltmeter. They normally have a low a.c. voltage range
(usually 1.999 volts full scale) which can be used to accurately
set the output of the signal generator at 1 volt r.m.s. You
need to be careful with the choice of calibration frequency
though. Most digital multimeters are only accurate at frequencies of up to a few hundred hertz. Setting the signal generator

for an output frequency of about 100Hz to 200Hz should give good results. Most analogue multimeters have a low a.c. voltage range, but it may not be low enough to permit a level of one volt r.m.s. to be set really accurately. This obviously depends on the quality of the instrument concerned. Many will allow this voltage level to be set with good accuracy.

Having set the signal generator to a suitable audio frequency, and having set its output level as accurately as possible to 1 volt r.m.s., you are ready to commence calibration. Start with both presets at roughly mid settings. First offset null control VR1 must be given the correct setting. In order to do this, first switch the unit to the 10 millivolt range and short circuit the input (to eliminate any stray pick up). You should find that by adjusting VR1 you can obtain a deflection of the meter which can be varied from zero to (probably) more than full scale deflection of ME1. Back-off VR1 just far enough to zero the meter. Turning it back too far will impair the accuracy of the unit at low readings, and so it is very important not to back it off excessively.

Next switch the millivoltmeter to its 1 volt range and feed it with the output of the signal generator. Then simply adjust VR2 for precisely full scale deflection on ME1. This completes the calibration process, and the unit is then ready for use.

In Use

Ordinary test prods are of little use with an instrument of this type. You should make up a set of test leads of the type described previously in the section of this chapter dealing with the test bench amplifier. Ready-made test leads of this type can be obtained, and they are usually fitted with BNC connectors. If you use test leads of this type, obviously SK1 must be a BNC socket, or the plug on the test leads must be removed and replaced with a 3.5 millimetre jack plug (or a plug to suit whatever type of socket you have used for SK1). Ready-made test leads are mostly excellent, but they are really intended for use with oscilloscopes. They are suitable for operation at frequencies of typically up to about 50MHz, and as a result of this they are rather over-specified for the present application, and are quite expensive.

An a.c. millivoltmeter can be used on its own for such things as checking the output levels from microphones, tuners, cassette decks, etc., or measuring noise levels. It is more usual for an instrument of this type to be used in conjunction with an audio signal generator though. As a simple example, assume that you wish to check the voltage gain of a pre-amplifier. The signal generator would be set to a suitable frequency (most audio testing is carried out at a middle audio frequency of around 800Hz to 1kHz), and then with the aid of the a.c. millivoltmeter it would be set for an appropriate output level.

It is important to choose a suitable input level. An excessive level could produce an output signal that is too strong to be measured by the millivoltmeter, although it might then be possible to measure it using a multimeter switched to a low a.c. voltage range. It is probably best to avoid high output levels though. These can cause clipping of the output signal which would give misleading readings. A low input level will probably give quite good results, but in an extreme case the noise level of the circuit under test could compromise the accuracy of readings. If you know that the preamplifier should have a gain of (say) 46dB (about 200 times), then an input level of 2 millivolt would seem about right. This gives an expected output voltage of 400 millivolts (2 millivolts x 200 = 400 millivolts). This is well within the maximum reading of the millivoltmeter, and is unlikely to overload the preamplifier.

Having set a suitable input level, it is then just a matter of measuring the output level. The voltage gain is equal to the output voltage divided by the input voltage. For instance, if the output level was measured at 575 millivolts, the voltage gain would be 287.5 times (575/2 = 287.5). If gain measured in decibels is required, decibel scales could be added to the meter's scale plate. This would be difficult to achieve in practice though. It is more realistic to make linear gain measurements and then convert them to decibels when necessary.

Frequency response testing is carried out in a similar fashion, but gain tests must be made at a range of frequencies. The results would then normally be plotted on a graph. Just how many test frequencies should be used depends on the frequency range involved and the attenuation rate of the filtering. A large number of test frequencies will ensure accurate results with no slight peaks or troughs in the response passing unnoticed. However, for much frequency response testing no more than a dozen measurements are needed in order to obtain an accurate representation of the test circuit's frequency response.

Chapter 2

METERS

What should undoubtedly be the first piece of electronic test equipment purchased by any electronics enthusiast is a multimeter. However, there are many electrical quantities that can be measured but which are not covered by most multimeters. A multimeter is an invaluable piece of test equipment, but it is not a universal panacea for all electronic ills. The audio millivoltmeter described in the previous chapter is an example of a form of metering that an ordinary multimeter can not handle properly. In this chapter we will look at a few other electronic test meters which fill in the gaps left by most multimeters.

Voltage Loading

The first project in this chapter is a high resistance voltmeter (also known as a high impedance voltmeter). This is a voltmeter which has a very high input impedance so that it does not tap off a significant amount of current from the circuit under test. It literally has a high resistance between its two test prods. In order to understand the significance of using a high resistance voltmeter you first need to consider what happens when you connect an ordinary multimeter to a test circuit. The sensitivity of an ordinary (analogue) multimeter is usually expressed as so many ohms per volt. Most analogue multimeters have a sensitivity of 20k per volt, but some inexpensive types have sensitivities as low as 1k per volt while some up-market instruments go as high as 100k per volt.

The sensitivity of a multimeter in this form is merely a means of expressing the resistance across the test prods. If a 20k per volt multimeter is switched to the 10 volt d.c. range, then the resistance across its test prods will be 200k (i.e. 20k x 10 volts = 200k). The resistance across the test prods of a 1k per volt meter on the same range would be just 10k (i.e. 1k x 10 volts = 10k).

A multimeter switched to a low voltage range is effectively just the meter movement plus a series resistor. Ideally the meter should have a very low full scale deflection current so that little current is tapped off from the circuit under test. In practice there is obviously a limit to how sensitive a meter movement can be made without it being impractically delicate. Consequently, few multimeters use a meter having a full scale value of less than 50 microamps (a figure which gives the standard 20k per volt sensitivity), and some use much less sensitive meters.

High sensitivity is not a factor that is always of great importance. When testing a high current circuit, such as the output of an audio power amplifier, the small amount of current tapped off by the meter should be totally insignificant. The same is not true of high impedance parts of a circuit. Consider the simple unity voltage gain buffer amplifier circuit of Figure 2.1. Resistors R1 and R2 bias the input of the amplifier to about half the supply voltage, or about 4.5 volts in this case. Measuring the output voltage of

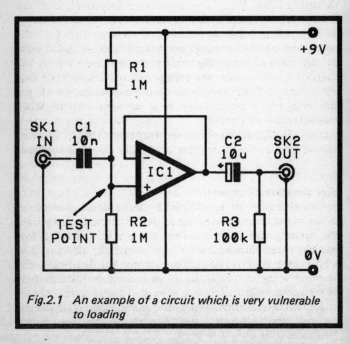

Fig.2.1   An example of a circuit which is very vulnerable to loading

IC1 should give an accurate reflection of the voltage here, since even a low power operational amplifier can supply the milliamp or less required to drive an analogue multimeter.

The situation is very different if the input voltage is measured. Connecting the negative test prod to the 0 volt supply rail in the usual way, and then connecting the positive test prod to the junction of R1, R2, etc., the resistance of the multimeter is effectively added in parallel with R2. Working out the resistance of the test meter and then doing a little calculating will soon provide the effective resistance of R2. We will not bother with any precise calculations here, but with using a 20k per volt multimeter on the 10 volt range to measure the voltage across R2, this gives 200k shunting R2. Its effective resistance must therefore be something under 200k, and the measured voltage would be under one-sixth of the supply voltage (since the effective resistance of R2 would constitute less than one-sixth of the total resistance through R1 and R2). This would obviously result in a very low reading — perhaps little more than 1 volt.

The reading is correct in that it is a true reflection of the voltage present at the test point, but it is erroneous in that it is only present while the multimeter is connected to the circuit. At other times the voltage will be completely different. Using a lower sensitivity multimeter such as a 1k per volt type the situation would be even worse. There would probably be no significant deflection of the multimeter's pointer at all! Again, the meter would be giving an accurate voltage reading, but one that was really totally misleading.

High Resistance Voltmeter

Improved results can be obtained by using an amplifier ahead of the meter circuit so that the amount of current drawn from the circuit under test is reduced, and a robust meter of low sensitivity can then be used. This is basically all there is to a high resistance voltmeter. They do not usually work on the basis of using the amplifier to provide a sensitive current meter action, and then adding several switched series resistors to provide several ranges. The more normal method is to have a circuit which requires a negligible input current, and which has an input sensitivity of (say) 1 volt full scale. Other ranges are provided by adding a switched attenuator ahead of the basic 0 to 1 volt meter circuit. The sensitivity of the meter in ohms per volt terms is very much dependent on the resistance through the attenuator. Also, as the input resistance is fixed, the ohms per volt sensitivity varies from one range to the next.

High resistance voltmeters normally have an input resistance of about 10 or 11 megohms, and as a couple of examples, this would give at least 10M per volt sensitivity on the 1 volt range, and 1M per volt on the 10 volt range. This obviously compares very well with a conventional 20k per volt multimeter. On the higher voltage ranges the ohms per volt sensitivity of a high resistance voltmeter is less impressive. It would be 100k per volt on the 100 volt range for example, which is not vastly better than a standard 20k per volt multimeter, and no better than a few high sensitivity multimeters. However, sensitivity on high voltage ranges tends to be less important than it is on low voltage ranges. With modern low voltage circuits most users make little use of the higher d.c. voltage ranges anyway.

If we apply a high resistance voltmeter to our earlier example, by shunting 10 or 11 megohms across R2 in the test circuit we are only marginally reducing its effective value. Readings will still be reduced by several percent, and loading is not a factor that can be totally ignored even when using a high resistance voltmeter, but there are few occasions when the degree of loading is large enough to give what could reasonably be considered misleading results.

High resistance analogue multimeters used to be quite common, but are something of a rarity these days. One reason for this is the popularity of digital multimeters. These are really a form of high resistance voltmeter, and normally have an input resistance of 10 to 11 megohms. In use, they must therefore be regarded as high resistance voltmeters, and results should not be assessed on the basis of significant loading on the test point. Despite the popularity of digital multimeters, there are still plenty of users who find analogue instruments quicker and easier to use. I must confess to preferring analogue instruments in many respects, but the greater ruggedness of digital instruments is an asset that should not be overlooked. Analogue instruments need to be treated with much greater respect if they are to provide long service.

The Circuit

This high resistance voltmeter is a simple three range analogue type having full scale values of 0.5, 5, and 50 volts. The input resistance is a little over 11 megohms. A definite advantage of digital multimeters over analogue types is that the former will respond to voltages of either polarity, whereas the latter must be connected to the test points with the correct polarity. This analogue design borrows from digital multimeter design philosophy in this respect, and it will accept an input voltage of either polarity. This is especially helpful when making measurements on equipment which has dual balanced supply rails. With this type of equipment test points can be of either polarity with respect to the central 0 volt earth rail. Having a meter that will respond to inputs of either polarity could give rise to confusing results, but an optional input polarity indicator circuit enables the polarity of the input signal to be positively identified.

Figure 2.2 shows the full circuit diagram for the high resistance voltmeter. The optional input polarity indicator circuit is shown in Figure 2.3. The main circuit is a full wave active rectifier, and it uses the same basic configuration that was described in the previous chapter. In this case the circuit does not need to provide high frequency operation, and there is no significant disadvantage in using silicon diodes in the bridge rectifier (D1 to D4). The advantages of silicon types is that they are cheaper and less easily damaged (particularly by heat when they are being soldered into circuit). D5 is a protection diode which ensures that the meter does not sustain any gross overloads. It might still be subjected to minor overloads, but any good quality meter should be able to take these without any risk of sustaining damage. VR1 is used to set the correct basic input sensitivity of 0.5 volts full scale.

The circuit is powered from a single 9 volt supply rather than the normal (for operational amplifier circuits) dual balanced supplies. R5 and R6 are used to effectively split the single 9 volt supply to provide dual 4.5 volt supplies. C1 provides negative feedback which severely limits the upper

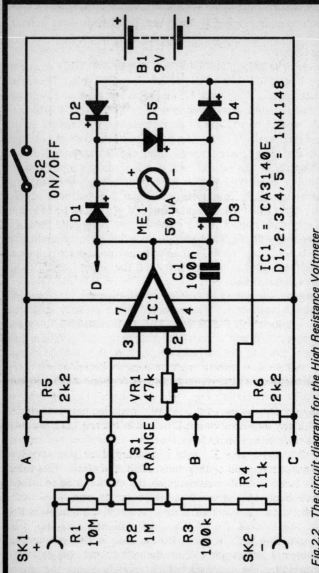

Fig.2.2 The circuit diagram for the High Resistance Voltmeter

48

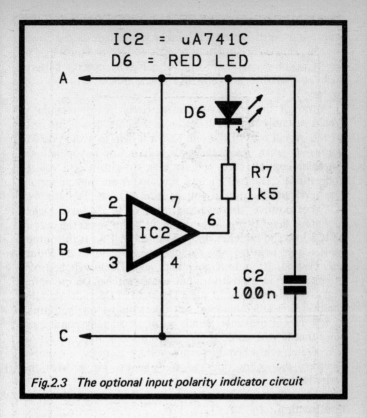

Fig.2.3 The optional input polarity indicator circuit

frequency response of the circuit. This helps to avoid problems
with any electrical noise picked up in the test leads producing
a strong deflection on ME1.

R1 to R4 plus S1 form a standard three step attenuator
giving attenuation rates of 0dB, 20dB, and 40dB. This enables
the basic 0.5 volt sensitivity of the circuit to be reduced by
factors of ten and one hundred, so as to give the 5 and 50
volt ranges. IC1 is a MOS input operational amplifier that has
an input resistance of over one million megohms. Thus,
despite the high resistor values used in the attenuator, it
does not significantly load the attenuator and reduce its
accuracy.

The current consumption of the circuit is only a few milli-amps, and a PP3 size 9 volt battery is adequate as the power source. However, if the unit is likely to receive a great deal of use it might be better to opt for a higher capacity battery, such as six HP7 size cells in a plastic holder or a PP9 size battery.

Although the polarity indicator circuit is not essential, I would certainly urge its inclusion in the unit. It will add little to the overall cost of the unit and will help to avoid possible confusion when using the unit. It is just an operational amplifier connected to operate as a straightforward voltage comparator. The two voltages it compares are the mid-supply bias level and the output voltage from IC1. If the output of IC1 goes positive, the inverting input of IC2 is taken higher in voltage than its non-inverting input. This sends the output of IC2 low and switches on l.e.d. indicator D6. If the output of IC1 goes negative, the comparative states of IC2's inputs are reversed, its output goes high, and D6 is switched off. In other words, a positive input signal switches D6 on, and a negative input switches it off. The state of D6 under standby conditions is indeterminate, but due to noise on the output of IC1 it will probably switch on under standby conditions. Note that if you would prefer D6 to have the opposite action (i.e. switch on when the input voltage is negative) simply reversing the connections to IC2's inputs will provide the desired action.

Construction

Details of the stripboard layout for the high resistance volt-meter project are provided in Figure 2.4, while the hard-wiring is shown in Figure 2.5. A stripboard having 31 holes by 14 copper strips is required. Construction of the board offers nothing out of the ordinary, but remember that IC1 is a MOS input device. Consequently, it must be fitted in an 8 pin d.i.l. holder and the other standard anti-static handling precautions should be observed. VR1 must be a miniature horizontal mounting preset if it is to fit into the board layout properly.

The attenuator resistors are mounted on S1 and not on the circuit board. Take care not to overheat these components and impair their accuracy when connecting them into circuit.

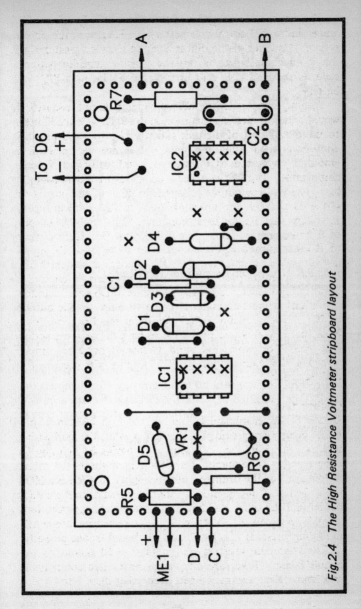

Fig.2.4 The High Resistance Voltmeter stripboard layout

51

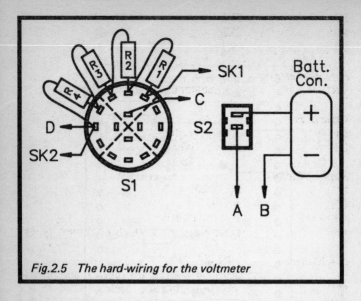

Fig.2.5   The hard-wiring for the voltmeter

These resistors should have a tolerance of 2% or better. 1%
resistors are probably worth the small extra cost. There should
be little difficulty in fitting the unit into a plastic or metal
box having dimensions of about 150 by 100 by 50 millimetres,
but this obviously assumes that the meter used for ME1 is not
a large type. A standard 60 millimetres by 40 millimetres (or
similar) meter should be perfectly adequate, but the accuracy
of the unit should be quite sufficient to justify a larger type if
preferred.

The drive current for D6 is not very great, and I would
recommend the use of a high brightness or ultra-bright l.e.d.
for this component.

Components for Figures 2.2 and 2.3

Resistors (all 0.25 watt 5% unless noted)
R1   10M 2% or better
R2   1M 2% or better
R3   100k 2% or better
R4   11k 2% or better

R5	2k2
R6	2k2
R7	1k5

Potentiometer

VR1	47k sub-miniature horizontal preset

Capacitors

C1	100n polyester
C2	100n ceramic

Semiconductors

IC1	CA3140E
IC2	μA741C
D1 to D5	1N4148 (5 off)
D6	5mm panel l.e.d. (high brightness type)

Miscellaneous

S1	3 way 4 pole rotary (only 1 pole used)
S2	SPST sub-miniature toggle
ME1	50μA moving coil panel meter
B1	9 volt (e.g. PP3 size)

Case about 150 x 100 x 50mm
0.1 inch matrix stripboard 31 holes by 14 copper strips
Control knob
Battery connector
Wire, solder, printed circuit pins, etc.

Calibration

In order to calibrate the unit you need an accurately known voltage that is something approaching the full scale voltage of one of the unit's ranges. As an example, a 4.5 volt battery could be used to provide a calibration voltage for the 5 volt range of the unit. An ordinary multimeter would be used to measure the true voltage provided by the battery. The high resistance voltmeter would then be connected to the battery, after which VR1 would be adjusted to give the correct voltage reading on ME1. Start with the wiper of VR1 set well towards the end of its track which connects to IC1 pin 2 and C1. This avoids having an excessive deflection of the meter when the unit is connected to the calibration source.

Note that the circuit has protection for the meter, but there is no input overload protection. There is little risk of damaging the unit when testing low voltage circuits, or when it is switched to the 5 or 50 volt ranges. Be careful not to have the unit on the 0.5 volt range when measuring potentials of a around 10 volts or more.

Transistor Tester
Probably the biggest omission from the repertoire of most multimeters is any means of testing components other than resistors and diodes. A few instruments have some form of built-in transistor tester, and a very few have capacitance measuring ranges, but most have no provision for testing either type of component. A transistor tester is one of the most useful pieces of test gear for the electronics enthusiast, and is something that can be built at quite low cost. Only a handful of components are required for a basic transistor tester, and the cost of the unit is largely dependent on the quality of the meter movement used. As high accuracy is not usually considered to be of prime importance for a transistor tester, a low cost type should be perfectly suitable.

Gain and Leakage
The basic setup for testing the d.c. current gain ("HFE" in transistor specifications) of a transistor is shown in Figure 2.6. Note that n.p.n. and p.n.p. transistors require different test circuits, and that these two configurations are shown in Figure 2.6(a) and Figure 2.6(b) respectively.

If we take the n.p.n. test circuit first, the supply is applied to the collector and emitter terminals of the test transistor with the appropriate polarity, and a meter (ME1) is used to monitor the current flow. A base current is supplied to the device via base resistor R1, with this component limiting the current to a suitable level. This level would normally be quite low — say about 1 to 100 microamps. The base current causes a much larger collector current to flow, and the current gain of a transistor is equal to its collector current divided by its base current. Thus, the higher the gain of the test transistor, the higher the reading on ME1. In fact ME1 can be calibrated

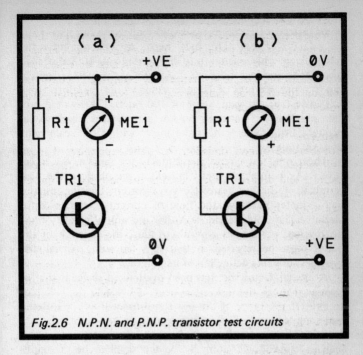

Fig.2.6 N.P.N. and P.N.P. transistor test circuits

directly in terms of current gain, and as a linear scale is obtained, no difficult recalibration of the meter is needed. Of course, this assumes that a suitable base current is chosen so that the current reading on ME1 is easily converted into the corresponding value for current gain.

It is not too difficult to arrange things in this way. For example, if a base current of 1 microamp is used, and ME1 has a full scale value of 1 milliamp (1000 microamps), the tester will have a full scale value of 1000. In other words, if the current reading in milliamps is translated into microamps, this gives the gain of the test device (which is equal to the collector current in microamps). Converting a reading of (say) 0.45 milliamps to a gain reading of 450 times is not a particularly complex process.

By having more than one base current available it is possible to give the unit several measuring ranges. If we extend our earlier example, using a base current of 10 microamps instead of 1 microamp would reduce the full scale value by a factor of ten. This must be so, as with ten times the base current only one-tenth of the current gain is then needed in order to produce full scale deflection of the meter. Switching to a base current of 10 microamps would therefore give a full scale (current gain) value of 100 times. This would provide much better accuracy on low gain devices which would produce little deflection of the meter with a full scale value of 1000 times.

The p.n.p. test circuit is essentially the same as the n.p.n. type. As before, an input current is supplied to the base terminal of the test transistor via a current limiting resistor, and a meter monitors the flow of current in the collector circuit. The only difference is that the supply polarity must be reversed. Also, as a result of this, the polarity of the meter must be reversed so that it is fed with a signal that provides forwards deflection of its pointer.

A crucial factor that has been overlooked so far is that of leakage through the test component. Obviously the collector to emitter resistance of the test transistor will not be infinite, and some current will flow between these two terminals even with no base current applied. For silicon transistors this leakage current will normally be too small to be of significance. A typical maximum leakage current for a silicon transistor would be 1 microamp, and a typical small signal silicon transistor might have a leakage level of perhaps 50 nanoamps (0.05 microamps). Germanium transistors tend to have relatively high leakage currents, with levels as high as one or two milliamps being acceptable in many cases. Some germanium power devices have quoted maximum acceptable leakage levels of around 100 milliamps!

Leakage currents are important for two reasons. Firstly, their effect on current gain readings must be taken into account. A transistor might be found to give quite a high current gain reading, but this would be deceptive if the leakage current was almost sufficient to give this gain reading. In order to obtain a realistic current gain figure the collector current must be reduced by an amount equal to the leakage current. In other words, the gain of a transistor is not really equal to the collector current divided by the base current. It is equal to the increase in collector current when a base current is applied, divided by that base current. Fortunately, in virtually all cases the leakage current is so low as to be of no consequence, and it can be ignored

The second reason for the leakage level being important is that it is often a strong pointer to whether or not a transistor is serviceable. This is especially the case with silicon transistors, where the leakage level is normally very low. If a silicon transistor is found to have a significant leakage level it almost certainly means that the device is unusable. Even if the gain of the device should be found to be quite acceptable, it is probably not worth using the component. It is quite likely to have other problems such as a high noise level, and reliability is unlikely to be very good. The data sheets for silicon transistors almost invariably quote very low maximum leakage levels, and any device which exceeds its leakage quota should be regarded with considerable suspicion.

Measuring the leakage current of a transistor is very easy, and simply requires a slight modification to the gain measuring setup. Either a switch should be included in the base circuit so that the base current can be switched off, or the base leadout wire can simply be left unconnected.

The Circuit

The full circuit diagram for the transistor tester appears in Figure 2.7. It follows the basic configuration of Figure 2.6 quite closely, but obviously n.p.n./p.n.p. switching has had to be incorporated. In fact any switching of this type for the meter has been avoided by incorporating a bridge rectifier here (D1 to D4). Whatever the polarity of the supply, two of the four diodes will always channel the current through the meter with the correct polarity. R4 is a current limiting resistor, and it ensures that the current through the meter is limited to a safe level (just under 2 milliamps) in the event of the test device being closed circuit. This permits a maximum overload on the meter of something approaching 100%, but this should not be sufficient to damage any moving coil meter, even if sustained for a long period of time.

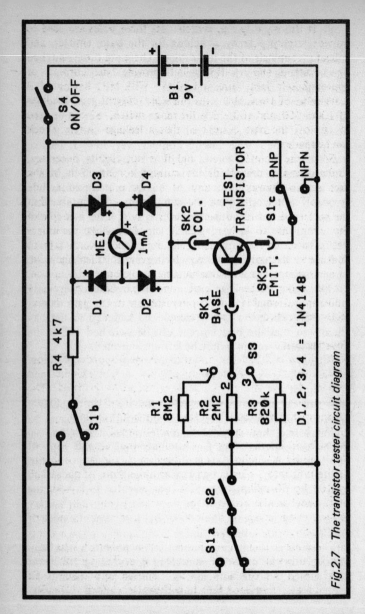

Fig.2.7 The transistor tester circuit diagram

58

S1 is the n.p.n./p.n.p. switch. Its three poles are used to provide supply polarity switching for the base, emitter, and collector terminals of the test device. There are three switched base resistors (R1 to R3) which provide base currents of approximately $1\mu A$, $4\mu A$, and $10\mu A$. With ME1 having a full scale value of 1mA, this gives full scale (current gain) readings of 1000, 250, and 100. S3 is the range switch. S2 can be used to cut off the base current so that a leakage current check can be made.

S4 is the on/off switch, and it is not strictly necessary. Under standby conditions the current consumption of the unit is zero anyway! However, it is good practice to include an on/off switch on any piece of equipment. This ensures that the battery is not run down unnecessarily if (say) a couple of the test prods should become short circuited while the unit is not in use. I have prematurely exhausted several sets of multimeter batteries in this way by leaving the instrument set to a resistance range. When in use the current consumption, except under meter overload conditions, never exceeds 1 milliamp. A small 9 volt battery such as a PP3 type is perfectly adequate as the power source.

Construction

With so few components, and such a large proportion of those components being panel mounted types such as switches and sockets, the use of a circuit board is not really justified. The unit can be hard-wired without too much difficulty. Figure 2.8 shows the wiring diagram for the transistor tester.

The best size of case for the unit is largely dependent on the size of the meter used. Assuming that a small type of about 60 by 40 millimetres is utilized, it should be possible to fit the unit into a plastic box having dimensions of about 150 by 100 by 50 millimetres. It is not essential to lay-out the front panel in the arrangement shown in Figure 2.8, but try to have things arranged sensibly so that a minimal number of long trailing wires are required.

There are a number of options available for SK1 to SK3. One of these is to mount a transistor socket on the front panel. This is convenient in that it should be possible to fit virtually any transistor into it without too much difficulty,

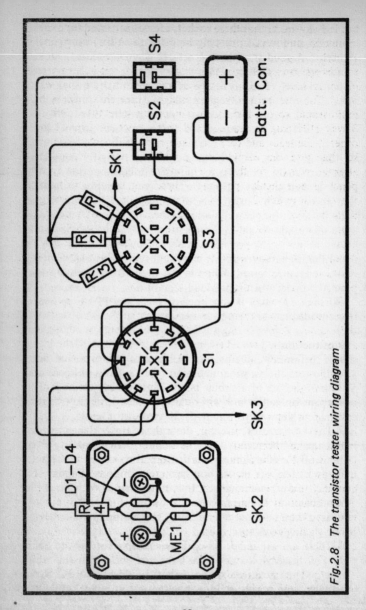

Fig.2.8 The transistor tester wiring diagram

60

but is awkward in that these sockets are not intended for panel mounting, and would probably be difficult to fix to the panel securely. A good alternative is a three way DIN socket. Most transistors can be plugged into one of these, and it is easy to make up a set of test leads to accommodate those that will not. The test leads merely consist of three short pieces of multi-strand (p.v.c. insulated) connecting wire fitted with a 3 way DIN plug at one end and three crocodile clips at the other. Use leads and (or) crocodile clips of different colours so that you can easily identify which is which. Another alternative is to fix three 1 millimetre sockets on the front panel in a triangular pattern. These can be used in much the same way as a 3 way DIN socket, but have the advantage that the test transistor should connect to them somewhat more easily and reliably. A final alternative is to simply drill a hole in the front panel for three short crocodile clip leads which are then hard-wired to the main unit. Once again, the leads and (or) the clips should be of different colours to permit easy identification.

Wiring up the unit is only likely to be a bit difficult because few constructors are familiar with this method of construction these days. Before fitting any of the components or adding in any of the wiring I would strongly recommend that all the tags should be tinned with solder. At least, those tags that are actually used should be tinned with solder. Only one pole of S3 is used, which leaves some twelve tags unused. Three poles of S1 are used, but it must be a type having an adjustable end-stop, which in this case is set for two way operation. This leaves seven tags of S1 unused. Note that S1 must be a "break before make" type, not a "make before break" switch. The latter would cause a momentary short circuit on the supply lines each time the switch was operated. This would almost certainly result in a very short contact life.

Construction is almost certainly easiest if all the components are fitted prior to adding any of the wiring. Add the two pairs of diodes on to ME1 (making sure their polarity is correct) and then add the two connections to complete the ring. Then add R4 and fit R1 to R3 onto S3. This should all be quite easy provided the ends of the component leads are tinned with solder before connecting them. Next add the

61

links that join certain pins of S1, and then add the point-to-point wiring plus the battery clip. This wiring must all be insulated in order to avoid any accidental short circuits. In fact I used non-insulated single strand wires for the links on S1, and this is an easy way of completing this wiring. However, if you do things this way you must be careful to route the links where they are well separated from one another, or p.v.c. sleeving must be fitted over them.

Components for Figure 2.7

Resistors (all 0.25W 5%)
R1	8M2
R2	2M2
R3	820k
R4	4k7

Semiconductors
D1	1N4148
D2	1N4148
D3	1N4148
D4	1N4148

Miscellaneous
ME1	1mA moving coil panel meter
S1	3 way 4 pole rotary with adjustable end-stop (set for 2 way operation, only 3 poles used)
S2	SPST sub-miniature toggle
S3	3 way 4 pole rotary (only one pole used)
S4	SPST sub-miniature toggle
B1	9 volt (PP3 size)
SK1, 2, 3	3 way DIN socket (see text)

Case about 150 x 100 x 50mm
Two control knobs
Battery connector
Wire, solder, etc.

In Use
Using the unit is basically quite simple, and it is just a matter of switching on, setting S1 for n.p.n. or p.n.p. operation (as

appropriate), connecting the test device correctly, checking the leakage current (S2 set open), and then measuring the gain of the device by setting S2 to the closed position. It is best to start with S3 at position 1 (the 0 to 1000 range), and to switch to one of the other ranges if a very low reading is obtained. It is unlikely that the test transistor will be damaged if S1 is set to the wrong mode, but due care should be exercised when testing germanium transistors. These are generally much less hardy than the more common silicon types. Of course, if the wrong mode is used it is quite likely that a "dud" will be indicated even if the test component is fully operational. When a "dud" device is indicated, always double check the control settings and connections to the device before discarding it.

Although using the unit is very straightforward, interpreting results is not necessarily as easy. In most cases it is, but some transistors are difficult to test. The high leakage levels of some germanium transistors and the difficulties they present were discussed earlier. Just what readings indicate a "dud" and what represents satisfactory test results are to some extent a matter of subjective judgement. It is possible for the leakage test to give an off-scale reading, but for the test device to be perfectly satisfactory. This is most likely to occur with power devices, and the leakage levels of small signal germanium transistors tend to be significant but still quite modest. Fortunately, germanium transistors are now largely obsolete, and you may never need to test one with the unit.

When testing any transistors using the unit you must bear in mind that current gains in data sheets are normally specified at certain collector voltages and currents. This tester does not provide checks at specific collector currents and voltages. Both depend on the meter indication obtained. The collector current is simply the one indicated on the meter. For instance, with the unit set to the 0 to 1000 range, and a reading of 0.45 milliamps being displayed, this represents a gain of 450 at a collector current of 0.45 milliamps (450 microamps). The collector voltage varies from about 8 volts at low readings to about 3 volts or so at high readings.

This is not all of academic importance. The gain of a transistor varies with changes in both collector current and voltage. Variations caused by changes in collector voltage tend to be relatively small, but changes in gain due to alterations in the collector current can be (and often are) quite substantial. In general, the gain of a transistor increases as its collector current is raised. This property is easily demonstrated by measuring the gain of a low gain transistor on the lowest and the highest ranges of the unit. The gain value indicated when using the 0 to 1000 range will almost certainly be much lower, due to the very much lower collector current that flows.

What this means in practice is that readings may well be slightly lower than the data sheets would suggest, simply because the transistors are being tested at lower collector currents. A marginally low gain reading could be indicative of a faulty component, but would be more likely to indicate that the device is at the low end of its gain range but acceptable in this respect. Power transistors are the ones where problems are most likely to be experienced. These generally have their current gains specified at quite high currents, and are only designed to work efficiently at these high currents. Quite low gain readings do not necessarily indicate a faulty device when checking power devices, but a gain reading that is only a small fraction of the minimum requirement probably does. If you are likely to test a lot of power devices it would be beneficial to have higher test currents. This is easily achieved by using a 10 milliamp meter for ME1, and reducing all four resistor values by a factor of ten. The only problem with doing this is that few component suppliers seem to stock a large range of panel meters these days, and a 10 milliamp type could be difficult to track down.

When using the unit you must bear in mind that it only provides approximate gain readings. This is all that is required in most cases as faulty transistors are not usually a little low in gain. Most faults produce a very low gain level. In fact in many cases faulty transistors are open or closed circuit, with the base terminal exercising no control on the collector current whatever.

Capacitance Meter

As pointed out in the previous section of this chapter dealing with the transistor tester, a serious omission from the repertoire of most multimeters is some means of measuring capacitance. It is possible to make a few basic tests on capacitors using the resistance range of a multimeter, but this really boils down to little more than checking that the test component has not developed a fault in its dielectric which has caused it to go closed circuit. With high value components it takes some time for the multimeter to charge the capacitor, and for the reading to go to a very high level. With a little experience the time taken for the reading to go off-scale can give a good idea of the test component's value. However, this simple test procedure only works reasonably well with high value capacitors, and does not normally work at all with capacitors of less than a few tens of nanofarads in value.

With so many capacitors used in electronic circuits, a capacitance meter is a decided asset for the electronics hobbyists' workshop. Units that provide a high degree of accuracy over a very wide capacitance range tend to be quite complex and expensive to build. For most purposes though, a unit that does not cover the highest and lowest value capacitors will suffice, and can be built at quite a modest cost. This unit has five capacitance ranges with full scale values of 1n, 10n, 100n, 1μ, and 10μ. Accuracy is very good except on the lowest range, where stray capacitance compromises results at the low value end of the range. The unit can still be used to test capacitors having values from a few tens of picofarads up to 10 microfarads. As explained previously, most multimeters can be used to check high value capacitors. This only leaves very low value capacitors uncatered for, and these are not used to any great extent in most types of modern electronic circuit. This unit plus a multimeter should therefore be capable of checking the vast majority of capacitors that you use.

Pulse Duration

Capacitance meters can operate on a variety of principles, but most simple units are based on a monostable multivibrator. The duration of the output pulse from the monostable is dependent on the values of the timing capacitor and the timing resistor. The pulse length is proportional to the values of both components. In this application the timing capacitance is the component under test, and the timing resistance is a reference component. This gives an output pulse duration that is proportional to the value of the test component, but some means of converting pulse length into a proportional meter reading is required.

This is actually quite easy, and can be achieved by using an oscillator to trigger the monostable at a fixed frequency. The waveforms of Figure 2.9 help to explain the manner in

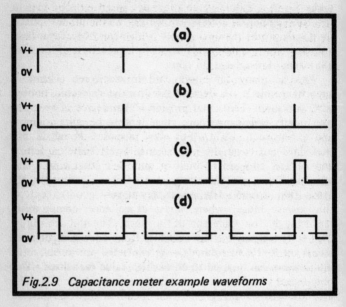

Fig.2.9   Capacitance meter example waveforms

which this gives the desired action. An important point to keep in mind here is that a moving coil panel meter fed with a pulse signal will not be able to follow the changes in input voltage unless they are at a very low frequency. With an input frequency of more than about 10Hz to 20Hz the meter registers the average input voltage.

In this example the waveform of (a) represents the very brief trigger pulses from the clock oscillator. The waveform of (b) is the output signal from the monostable with no test capacitor connected. Stray capacitance prevents a pulse width of zero from being obtained, but the pulses are so short as to give a negligible average output voltage. In (c) a test capacitor is connected, and it gives a mark space ration of 1 to 7. This in turn gives an average output voltage equal to one-eighth of the supply voltage (as indicated by the dot-dash line), since the output is low for 87.5% of the time and high for the other 12.5%. In (d) a test capacitor of double the previous value has been connected to the unit, and the longer pulse duration has resulted in a mark-space ratio of 1 to 3. The average output voltage is now 25% of the supply voltage, as the output of the monostable is high for 25% of the time. In other words, a doubling of the test capacitance has doubled the average output voltage.

Provided the pulse duration does not become excessively long, this gives the required pulse duration to voltage conversion. If the pulse duration should become excessive, the result is a sort of frequency divider action, with the monostable only triggering on (say) every second clock pulse. The average output voltage drops back to a relatively low level if this should happen. However, provided the output pulse duration never exceeds the period of one clock cycle, the desired action with good linearity is obtained.

The Circuit

Figure 2.10 shows the full circuit diagram for the capacitance meter, which is based on a couple of the ever popular 555 timer integrated circuits (IC1 and IC2). In fact these are an "improved" version of the standard 555, the TLC555P. This is a low power version of the 555, but in this case it is the higher speed and lower self-capacitance that are of prime importance. These help to improve performance on the lowest range. The self-capacitance of a standard 555 seems to be around 50p, whereas the TLC555P would seem to have a self-capacitance that is usually well under 20p. This ensures that any deflection of the meter under standby conditions on range 1 is too low to greatly detract from the accuracy of the unit.

IC1 is the clock oscillator, and accordingly it is operated in the astable mode. It is not quite the standard astable configuration in that there would normally be a resistor between pins

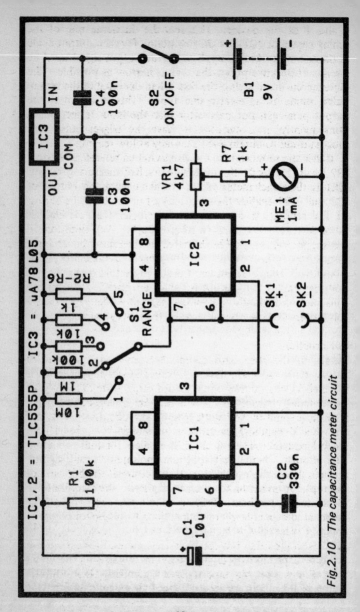

Fig.2.10 The capacitance meter circuit

68

6 and 7 of the device. This sets the discharge rate of the timing capacitor (C2), or the low period for each output cycle in other words. In this application the output signal must be a series of negative pulses that are as narrow as possible. The salient point here is that the 555 when operated in the monostable mode is a retriggerable type. This means that the output pulse can not be shorter than the input trigger pulse. Consequently, it is essential to have the trigger pulse very short in order to obtain good accuracy at low readings.

IC2 is the monostable, and five switched reference resistors (R2 to R6) provide the unit with its five measuring ranges. ME1 is the panel meter which is driven from the output of IC2, and VR1 enables the sensitivity of the meter to be adjusted for calibration purposes. It is crucial that the unit is powered from a very well stabilised supply. Any variations in the supply voltage will be reflected in corresponding changes in readings. The unit is powered from a 9 volt battery, but monolithic voltage regulator IC3 stabilises this to produce a well regulated 5 volt output for the main circuit. The current consumption is only a few milliamps, and a small (PP3 size) 9 volt battery is perfectly adequate as the power source.

Construction

Details of the stripboard component panel are provided in Figure 2.11. A board having 32 holes by 15 copper strips is required. Construction of the board offers little that is out of the ordinary. Although IC1 and IC2 are CMOS components, they have built-in anti-static protection circuits that render any special handling precautions unnecessary. I would still recommend the use of 8 pin d.i.l. hodlers for these components though. Note that they are mounted "upside-down" (i.e. pin 1 and the notch of each device are at the bottom not the top). A dozen link wires are required — be careful not to overlook any of them. Printed circuit pins are fitted to the board at the points where connections to off-board components will eventually be made.

As with the other projects that use a meter, the best size for the case depends to a large extent on the size of the meter used. For a unit that incorporates a standard 60 x 40 millimetre panel meter, or one of about this size, a plastic box

x = Break In Strip

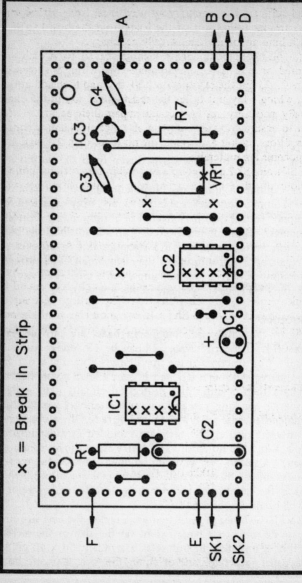

Fig.2.11   The capacitance meter stripboard layout

70

having dimensions of about 150 by 100 by 50 millimetres should suffice. The exact layout used is far from critical, but try to arrange things so that the leads from the board to SK1 and SK2 are no longer than is really necessary.

The off-board components include R2 to R6 which are mounted on S1. The point-to-point style wiring is shown in Figure 2.12. Fit the resistors onto S1 first and then add in the other wiring. Try not to let the resistors get any hotter than is really necessary, as heat could impair their accuracy. In order to ensure good accuracy on all ranges it is important to use resistors having a tolerance of no more than 2%, and 1% components are preferable.

If SK1 and SK2 are a couple of 1 millimetre sockets mounted close together on the front panel, many capacitors will connect to them directly. For those that will not, a pair of short crocodile clip leads must be made up. It is important that these leads are quite short (preferably no more than 50 millimetres long), as long leads could reduce the accuracy of the unit with low value capacitors. The unit can be used to test polarised (electrolytic and tantalum capacitors), but these components must be connected the right way round if reliable results are to be obtained. The positive leadout is the one that connects to SK1. It is a good idea to use a red socket for SK1 and a black one for SK2, so that the correct polarity is clearly indicated.

Components for Figure 2.10

Resistors (all 0.25W 5% unless noted)

R1	100k
R2	10M 1 or 2%
R3	1M 1 or 2%
R4	100k 1 or 2%
R5	10k 1 or 2%
R6	1k 1 or 2%
R7	1k

Potentiometer

VR1	4k7 sub-min hor preset

71

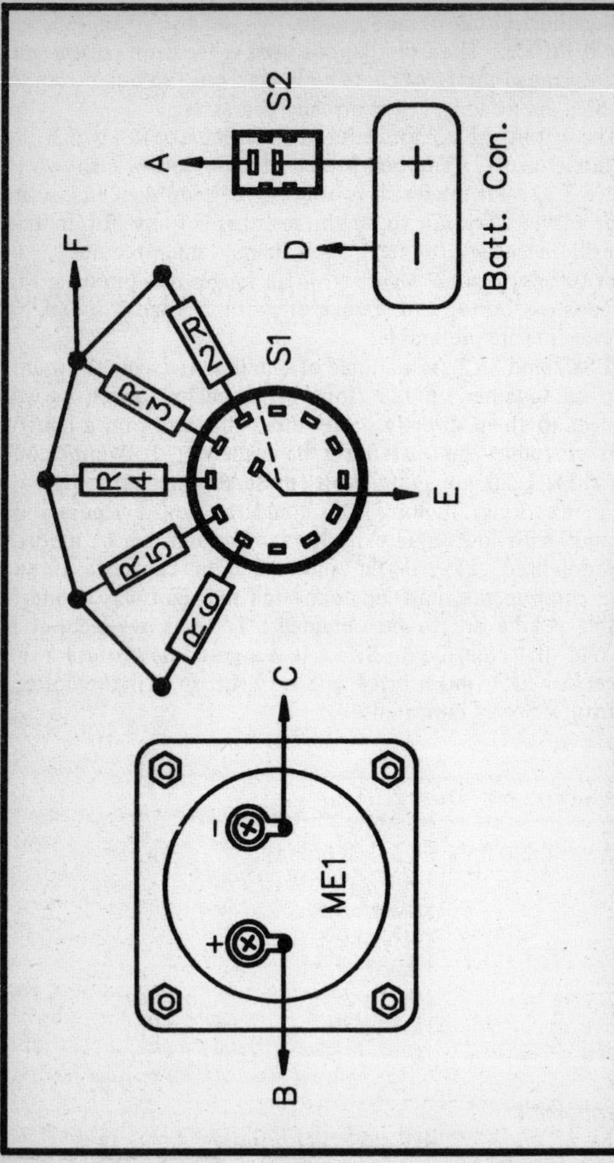

Fig.2.12 The wiring diagram for the capacitance meter

Capacitors

C1	10μ 25V radial elect
C2	330n polyester
C3	100n ceramic
C4	100n ceramic

Semiconductors

IC1	TLC555P
IC2	TLC555P
IC3	μA78L05 (5V 100mA positive regulator)

Miscellaneous

ME1	1mA moving coil panel meter
B1	9 volt (PP3 size)
S1	1 pole 12 way with adjustable end-stop (set for 5 way operation)
S2	SPST sub-min toggle
SK1	1mm socket (red)
SK2	1mm socket (black)

Case about 150 x 100 x 50 millimetres
Stripboard having 32 holes by 15 copper strips
Battery connector
Control knob
Two 8 pin d.i.l. i.c. holders
Wire, solder, etc.

Calibration

The first point that must be made is that the unit should never be used to test a capacitor that is charged up. This is especially important when testing high value or high voltage components. This is not just a failing of this capacitance meter — virtually all instruments of this type are vulnerable to damage from charged-up test components. The simplest solution to the problem is to short circuit the leads of each test component together prior to connecting them to the capacitance meter. A metal plate fixed to the top panel of the unit can be used for components that have short leadouts which can not be connected together.

A better solution is to have an extra pair of sockets and test leads, with a 33 ohm current limiting resistor wired between the two sockets. This will provide a more gradual (but still quite rapid) discharge that will avoid the sparking that occurs with a simple short circuit of the capacitor. Of course, it is only when testing a capacitor that has just been removed from a piece of equipment that has recently been powered-up that there is any great danger of the test capacitor holding a significant charge. On the other hand, it does no harm to always play safe and ensure that test components are fully discharged. Bear in mind that high voltage capacitors are extremely dangerous when charged up, and that they may retain their charge for some considerable period of time after the equipment in which they are installed has been switched off. Only those with suitable experience should attempt to remove and test a component of this type.

In order to calibrate the unit you require a close tolerance (1 or 2%) capacitor having a value equal to the full scale value of one range of the capacitance meter. It is not a good idea to calibrate the unit on range 1 as the accuracy on this range is not quite as good as that obtained on the other ranges. Calibration on ranges 4 and 5 can not be recommended either. Close tolerance capacitors having a value of 1μ or 10μ could be difficult to obtain, and extremely expensive indeed if you could find sources of supply. Calibration on range 2 using a 10n capacitor or range 3 using a 100n component are more practical propositions.

The calibration process merely involves switching on the unit and setting it to the appropriate range, connecting the calibration capacitor to SK1 and SK2, and then adjusting VR1 for precisely full scale deflection of the meter.

When testing capacitors using any capacitance meter, bear in mind that the tolerances of many capacitors are quite high. In particular, ceramic and electrolytic types can have tolerances as large as plus 100% and minus 50%. Relatively few types seem to offer tolerances of less than 20%. With some capacitors a substantial error in value is therefore quite acceptable.

AF Frequency Meter
The ideal piece of test gear for frequency measurement is a digital instrument having a wide range of gate times, and with

the capability of operating at frequencies of up to at least a few hundred megahertz. Unfortunately, despite general reductions in the prices of electronic equipment, high quality digital frequency meters (d.f.m.s) remain quite expensive. In fact the lowest cost d.f.m.s are still far from cheap.

For audio frequency measurement an analogue frequency meter, based on an ordinary moving coil panel meter, is often capable of giving sufficiently accurate results. Apart from use as a test instrument for frequency measuring applications, a unit of this type can be very useful as a frequency readout for an audio frequency signal generator. It is particularly useful for operation in conjunction with a home constructed audio signal generator where providing an accurately calibrated frequency scale can be difficult and very time consuming.

This audio frequency meter covers frequencies up to 100kHz. It has four ranges with full scale values of 100Hz, 1kHz, 10kHz, and 100kHz. It is quite sensitive, and requires a minimum input level of under 10 millivolts peak-to-peak in order to function properly. A trigger circuit ensures that the unit cuts out if the input level is inadequate, rather than giving a low and erroneous reading. The input impedance is quite high at about 500 kilohms (it is inevitably somewhat lower at high frequencies due to the shunting effect of the input capacitance).

Basic Operation

The basic way in which the unit functions is very similar to the system used in the capacitance meter project described previously. The output from a monostable is fed to a voltmeter circuit that registers the average output voltage. The difference is that in this case the pulse duration of the monostable is fixed, and it is the trigger frequency that alters. The trigger frequency is, of course, equal to the frequency of the input signal. With a low input frequency there is a large gap from one pulse to the next, and the average output voltage is low. With a much higher input frequency the pulses become bunched together and the average output voltage becomes much higher. In fact there is a linear relationship between the input frequency and the average output voltage, giving the required frequency to voltage conversion. Although

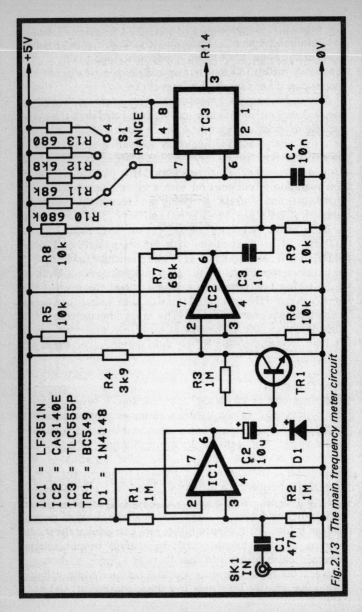

Fig.2.13 The main frequency meter circuit

IC1 = LF351N
IC2 = CA3140E
IC3 = TLC555P
TR1 = BC549
D1 = 1N4148

76

this is a very simple method of voltage to frequency conversion, at the low frequencies involved in audio applications it gives very good linearity, and is not easily bettered.

The Circuit
Figure 2.13 shows the main circuit diagram for the analogue frequency meter. The meter and regulator circuits are shown separately in Figure 2.14.

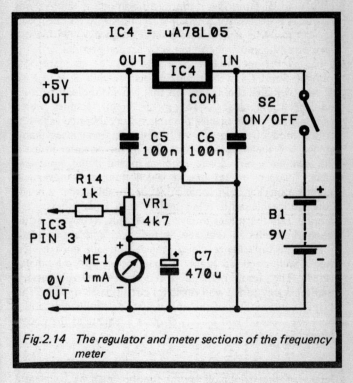

Fig.2.14 The regulator and meter sections of the frequency meter

IC1 acts as the basis of the input stage which is a simple operational amplifier voltage follower circuit. This provides no voltage gain, but provides the unit with a high input impedance. TR1 operates in the common emitter mode, and this provides most of the circuit's voltage gain (over 40dB of

voltage gain in fact). IC2 is a Schmitt trigger circuit with
hysteresis provided by R7. This stage ensures that the monostable is not triggered at all if the input signal is marginally too
low, so that low and misleading readings are avoided. It also
helps to avoid multiple triggering if an unusual or badly noise
infested waveform is applied to the input. Bear in mind
though, that the hysteresis has only a limited effect. A lot of
noise on the input signal could result in misleading results. A
really unusual input waveform might also defeat the hysteresis, but it is debateable whether waveforms with double peaks
etc. can really be said to have a single frequency. With most
waveforms the unit will give perfectly accurate results.

IC3 is the monostable, and this uses the standard 555
configuration. C4 is the timing capacitor, while R10 to R13
are four switched timing resistors that provide the unit with its
four measuring ranges. The meter circuit includes preset
resistor VR1 which enables the unit to be calibrated against a
known input frequency. At low input frequencies many
moving coil meters get a severe case of the "pointer jitters".
This can be a very severe problem indeed if the input frequency happens to hit one at which the meter movement
exhibits a mechanical resonance. It is a problem that is much
more noticeable with some meters than with others. C7
smooths out the pulses to give a reasonably ripple-free signal
across the meter so that any "jitter" problems are avoided.

Like the capacitance meter project, this one must be fed
from a well stabilised supply if good accuracy is to be main-
tained. The circuit is therefore fed from the 9 volt battery
supply by way of a 5 volt regulator circuit based on IC4. The
current consumption of the unit is just a few milliamps, and a
small (PP3 size) 9 volt battery is quite adequate as the power
source.

Construction
Details of the stripboard layout for the analogue frequency
meter are provided in Figure 2.15. This requires a board
having 41 holes by 16 copper strips. The wiring diagram is
shown in Figure 2.16. Construction is much along the lines of
the other projects in this chapter, and there is little that merits
any special mention. Note though that IC3 has the opposite

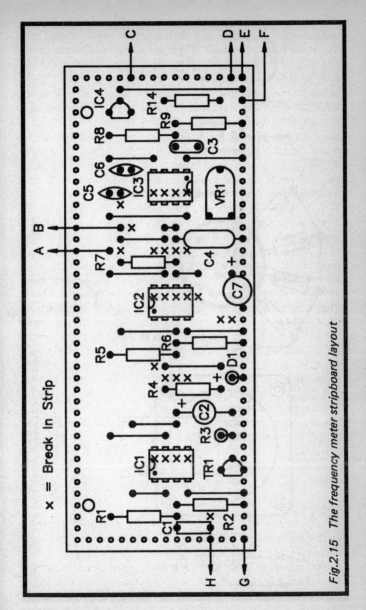

Fig.2.15 The frequency meter stripboard layout.

x = Break In Strip

79

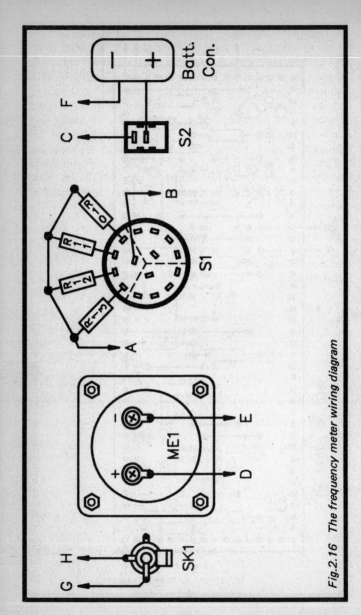

Fig.2.16 The frequency meter wiring diagram

orientation to the other two 8 pin d.i.l. integrated circuits. Be careful to fit it the right way round. IC2 is a MOS input device that consequently requires the standard anti-static handling precautions to be observed. In Figure 2.16 it is assumed that SK1 is a standard 3.5 millimetre jack socket, but any other type of audio/test equipment connector could be used here if preferred. S1 is one pole of a standard 4 way 3 pole rotary switch. Construction is easier if C1 has 7.5 millimetre lead spacing and C3 has 5 millimetre lead spacing. Otherwise it could be difficult to fit these components into the layout. Ideally C4 should be a type which has fairly long leadouts, but if necessary extension leads can be soldered to it.

Components for Figures 2.13 and 2.14

Resistors (all 0.25W 5% unless noted)

R1	1M
R2	1M
R3	1M
R4	3k9
R5	10k
R6	10k
R7	68k
R8	10k
R9	10k
R10	680k 1 or 2%
R11	68k 1 or 2%
R12	6k8 1 or 2%
R13	680 1 or 2%
R14	1k

Potentiometer

VR1	4k7 sub-min hor preset

Capacitors

C1	47n polyester (7.5 mm lead spacing)
C2	10µ 25V radial elect
C3	1n mylar (5mm lead spacing)
C4	10n polyester (C280)

C5	100n ceramic
C6	100n ceramic
C7	470µ 10V radial elect

Semiconductors

IC1	LF351N
IC2	CA3140E
IC3	TLC555P
IC4	µA78L05 (5V 100mA reg)
TR1	BC549
D1	1N4148

Miscellaneous

S1	4 way 3 pole rotary (only one pole used)
S2	SPST sub-min toggle
B1	9 volt (PP3 size)
ME1	1mA moving coil panel meter
SK1	3.5mm jack socket

Case about 150 x 100 x 50mm
Stripboard having 41 holes by 16 copper strips
Control knob
Battery connector
Three 8 pin d.i.l. integrated circuit holders
Wire, solder, etc.

Calibration

In order to calibrate the unit you must have access to a signal at a known frequency that will give 50 to 100% deflection of the meter on any range of the unit. Ideally a calibration oscillator or an accurately calibrated audio signal generator would be used to provide the calibration signal. In the absence of suitable test equipment an electronic musical instrument should suffice. For example, the A above middle A is at a frequency of 880Hz. This could be used to calibrate the unit on range 2. Simply couple the input of the instrument to SK1, then get a helper to play the A above middle A on the instrument while you adjust VR1 for a reading of 880Hz.

When using the unit keep in mind that inputs of more than a few volts peak-to-peak could cause overloading, which could possibly lead to inaccurate results. In an extreme case the input circuit of the unit could be overloaded to the point where it sustains damage. The unit can only be used to test high signal levels if it is used in conjunction with a probe having a built-in attenuator. Oscilloscope probes having an integral 20dB switchable attenuator are ideal, but far from cheap. A test probe having a series resistor of about 33k should be adequate to ensure correct operation and prevent damage on any high level input signals that are likely to be encountered.

Chapter 3

PROBING

There is an old joke in the electronics world about the term
"portable" meaning "its got a handle", rather than that the
equipment is particularly light and easy to move around.
Even with modern miniaturisation I suppose that it is still
true that some items of so-called portable equipment are
something less than pocketable. Some seem quite easy to
move around until the ten or twelve "D" size rechargeable
batteries are added, roughly doubling the weight! However,
there are plenty of genuinely portable and truly miniature
items of equipment, made possible by modern components
and low power circuits.

In the field of test gear this miniaturisation has led to the
development of some popular "probe" type devices. Probably
the best known of these are the logic probes, which indicate
the logic level present at the test point. However, there are
other types of probe tool such as analogue probes, which are
a simple form of voltage measuring device. In this final
chapter a few probe type circuits are described — two logic
probes and one analogue type.

In fact these circuits do not have to be built as probes, and
could be constructed in standard cases with connections to
the circuit under investigation being made via standard screened test leads. There is an advantage to probe type tools in
some applications, apart from their small size and excellent
portability. This is that the capacitance of the screened lead
can be avoided. Although this capacitance is unlikely to be
very large, it can still be quite significant when testing high
frequency circuits, and this includes logic circuits where this
capacitance can slow down transitions from one logic level to
the other.

A probe type piece of test equipment is really just an extension of the screened test leads idea. Probe tools usually take
the general form outlined in Figure 3.1. The metal prod at the
front of the unit is the non-earthy input, and an earth lead
plus clip connect to the chassis of the equipment under test in

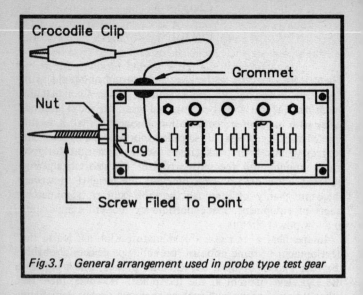

Fig.3.1   General arrangement used in probe type test gear

the usual manner. Instead of having the signal coupled to the main circuit via a screened lead, the circuit is included in the probe assembly. As a result of this there are no long connecting leads, no screened cables are required, and the capacitance of the screen lead is avoided.

Home Constructor Probes

There are definite advantages to probe style test equipment, but it has to be admitted that they can be a bit awkward to construct. There are numerous project cases available, but few are specifically designed for this type of application. Some of the smaller ordinary cases can be used in probe style projects without too much difficulty. The main problem is in finding something to act as the prod at the front of the unit. The method I have found to be the easiest is to use a long 6BA or M3 screw. A screw 25 millimetres long is about the shortest that is likely to be usable, and I would recommend the use of one about double this length if you can obtain it. In fact an even longer screw might prove useful for reaching connection points in inaccessible places, but the chances of obtaining one are probably not very good. A soldertag fitted on the screw inside the case represents an easy way of making a connection to the screw. If you require the usual pointed style test prod, some careful filing of the screw should produce the desired result. However, file the screw once it has been fitted to the case, not beforehand otherwise you may find that it is impossible to fit the fixing nut on to the screw. Figure 3.1 illustrates this general method of assembly.

Of course, if you search through a few component catalogues you may well find one or two cases intended for probe type circuits, and complete with the prod section. Where possible it is probably best to use one of these, but these cases will not necessarily be the right size and shape for the circuit board you wish to fit into them.

Analogue Probe

An analogue probe is a simple voltage measuring tool for making quick checks on equipment. It would be possible to have a miniature moving coil meter built into the probe, or a small digital readout. Most units of this type have a simple l.e.d. display though, often with just a few l.e.d.s indicating whether or not the input voltage is above certain threshold levels. This unit has ten l.e.d.s which have threshold voltages of 1 to 10 volts with one volt increments between l.e.d.s. It has what is generally termed a "bargraph" display, although in this case it is not strictly speaking a true bargraph. The display operates in the "dot" mode, which means that only one l.e.d at a time is switched on. If (say) the input potential is five volts, then l.e.d. number five will switch on, but l.e.d.s one to four will be switched off. This is not quite such a clear indication as a true bargraph display, but it has the advantage of keeping the current consumption down to more manageable proportions. This is especially important for a probe circuit where the use of a large battery is obviously out of the question.

Although a voltmeter with a single 0 to 10 volt range and only 1 volt resolution might seem too restricted to be of any practical value, it should be kept in mind that many home constructor projects are powered from 5 to 9 volt supplies, and that precise voltage measurements are not required in many instances. Often you only need something like "is the test point at about half the supply voltage?", rather than the exact voltage to the nearest millivolt. A unit of this type is not a replacement for a good quality multimeter, but it is a useful little aid for quick checks on many types of circuit. A useful feature of this unit is that it has a high input resistance of around 11 megohms. It is therefore a form of high resistance voltmeter, and as such it will place very little loading on the test points.

The Circuit

Refer to Figure 3.2 for the full circuit diagram of the analogue probe. This is based on the popular LM3914N bargraph driver (IC2). This device contains a voltage reference, decoder and driver circuits for the display, in fact just about everything needed apart from the display. The latter is formed by l.e.d.s D1 to D10, which are ordinary panel mounting l.e.d.s mounted in a row. The l.e.d. current is controlled by internal constant current generators, and these are controlled by discrete resistor R3. This sets the l.e.d. current at about 10 milliamps, which gives good l.e.d. brightness without giving the unit an excessive current consumption. Pin 9 of IC2 is wired to pin 11 in order to set the device to "dot" mode operation.

The LM3914N is quite sensitive, and in its normal operating mode it only requires an input of 1.2 volts in order to light the tenth l.e.d. of the display. The input impedance of the device is not very high though. Consequently, in this circuit it is preceded by an attenuator and a buffer amplifier based on IC1. VR1 is part of the attenuator, and it is adjusted to give the correct sensitivity. By using other values for R2 and VR1 it is possible to accommodate other full scale sensitivities. For example, with these components at a value of 470k it should be possible to set up VR1 for a full scale potential of 20 volts (which gives 2 volt resolution).

The current consumption of the circuit is about 7 milliamps under standby conditions, or about 17 milliamps when one of the display l.e.d.s is activated. This can be supplied by a PP3 size 9 volt battery, although there may be some advantage in

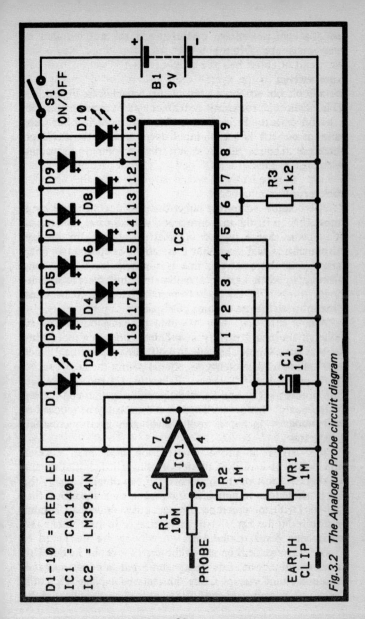

Fig.3.2 The Analogue Probe circuit diagram

D1-10 = RED LED
IC1 = CA3140E
IC2 = LM3914N

89

using a high power type, especially if the unit is likely to receive a great deal of use.

Construction

Details of the stripboard layout are provided in Figure 3.3. This requires a board having 50 holes by 17 copper strips. This can conveniently be a piece cut from a standard 5 inch long stripboard. IC1 is a MOS input operational amplifier, and it therefore requires the usual anti-static handling precautions. Although IC2 is not a MOS device, it is not particularly cheap either. Consequently, I would strongly urge the use of a socket for this component.

The board is somewhat larger than its ideal size, making it impossible to fit the unit into a really small case. One reason for this is that I used 5 millimetre l.e.d.s in the display. Although it would seem that these could be spaced two holes apart (5.08 millimetres), this is not possible. The body diameter of each l.e.d. is 5 millimetres, but there is a wider ring at the rear of the body to permit fixing into panel clips. This enforces the use of three hole spacing.

With a little ingenuity it would probably be possible to redesign the board slightly in order to produce a more compact layout. Simply changing to a different type of l.e.d., such as 3 millimetre diameter types, should permit the l.e.d. spacing to be reduced to 0.2 inches. Relocating C1 and the connection points to B1— and S1 might permit a further contraction of the board. In fact its length could probably be reduced to well under 4 inches if really small size is of paramount importance.

The basics of probe construction have been covered previously. It is really a matter of using a little initiative, and making the most of the materials you can obtain. Ideally the board should be mounted in the case in such a position that D1 to D10 can protrude through holes drilled at suitable positions in the case. An alternative is to have them just below one panel of the case. A window for the l.e.d.s to "look" through is then cut in the case above the l.e.d.s. This window should be fitted with some red window material. About the only way of fixing this material in place is to cut it substantially over-size, and to then glue it in place behind the

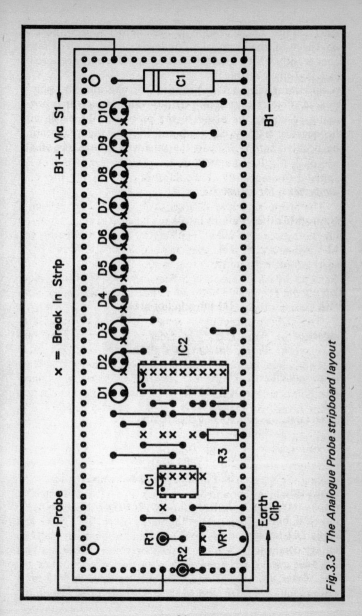

x = Break In Strip

Probe

B1+ Via S1

B1−

Earth Clip

Fig.3.3 The Analogue Probe stripboard layout

91

panel cutout, being careful to only apply adhesive near to the edges of the material. Window material is often made from a fairly brittle grade of plastic, and due care needs to be exercised when cutting it.

No wiring diagram is provided for this project, simply because there is very little point-to-point wiring. It is just a matter of wiring the board to the probe tip, the earth clip, the negative battery clip lead, and S1, and then connecting the positive battery lead to the otherwise unused tag of S1.

Components for Figure 3.2

Resistors (all 0.25 watt 5%)
R1   10M
R2   1M
R3   1k2

Potentiometer
VR1   1M sub-min hor preset

Capacitor
C1 10μ 25V axial elect

Semiconductors
IC1   CA3140E
IC2   LM3914N
D1 to D10   Red l.e.d.s (10 off)

Miscellaneous
B1   9 volt (PP3 size)
S1   SPST sub-min toggle
Small case
Stripboard having 50 holes by 17 copper strips
8 pin DIL holder
18 pin DIL holder
Battery connector
Crocodile clip
Wire, solder, etc.

Calibration

With a resolution of only 1 volt the unit does not require any particularly precise calibration. Results will probably be satisfactory if the probe tip is temporarily wired to the positive supply rail of the unit, and VR1 is then adjusted to switch on D9. If you require optimum accuracy from the unit, you must provide an accurate calibration potential equal to a whole number of volts. For example, a project which has a stabilised 5 volt supply can be used to provide an accurate 5 volt calibration voltage. VR1 would then be adjusted to light up D5. There will be a narrow range of settings over which this l.e.d. would switch on, and VR1 would be set as close as possible to the middle of this range.

It is worth reiterating here the dangers of making tests on mains powered equipment. You should certainly not do so unless you are quite sure you know exactly what you are doing. A unit of this type should never be used to make checks on equipment which has its chassis connected to one side of the mains supply.

CMOS Probe

In its most basic form a logic probe is a passive device using one or two l.e.d.s to indicate the logic level at the test point. While such a unit is very cheap and simple, it is not without some severe drawbacks. One of these is merely that the current needed to drive the l.e.d. or l.e.d.s at reasonable brightness might be more than some logic outputs could reasonably be asked to supply. Most logic outputs are actually quite capable of driving a l.e.d., but it has to be borne in mind that any outputs being tested may already be loaded to something approaching the maximum acceptable level.

Another drawback of a passive logic probe, and one shared by some of the more simple active probe designs, is that brief and infrequent pulses are unlikely to be detected. This is a major drawback as many logic circuits deal largely in signals of this type. A very brief signal will either fail to light the l.e.d. due to inadequacies in the switching speed of the l.e.d., or in a less extreme case the l.e.d. will in fact pulse on, but the resultant flash will be too brief to be perceived by the human eye.

This active logic probe has three l.e.d.s to indicate the logic state at the test point. Two of these l.e.d.s merely indicate logic 0 and logic 1, as appropriate. If the input signal is a continuous pulse type of some form, then both l.e.d.s will probably switch on. With an input signal having a 1 : 1 mark-space ratio the two l.e.d.s will switch on at equal brightness. With any other mark-space ratio there will be a bias with the input signal spending more time at one logic level than the other. This is reflected in the brightness of the l.e.d.s with the one having the input signal at its logic state for the greater amount of the time being brighter than the other l.e.d. Thus it is possible to roughly gauge the mark-space ratio of the input signal from the relative brightness of the l.e.d.s. Of course, the input signal may not be a regular waveform, but the comparative brightness of these two l.e.d.s will still indicate any bias towards one logic level or the other. As the bias varies, so will the relative brightness of the two l.e.d.s.

The third l.e.d. is activated when an input pulse is detected. Even if the input pulse is only very brief, the l.e.d. will still be switched on for around a second, so that a clear indication of the input pulse is provided. Thus, even with something like a 500ns pulse every two seconds, the third l.e.d. will clearly indicate each input pulse. It is possible (but unlikely) that the input signal could be between the maximum legal logic 0 voltage, and the minimum valid logic 1 level, and that this would cause the other two l.e.d.s to switch on at about half brightness. Obviously the other two l.e.d.s switched on at about half brightness could give the impression that the input signal was a pulse signal with a mark-space ratio of about 1 : 1. However, the absence of any indication from the third l.e.d. would show that no input pulses were present, and that the input signal was a static one at an invalid voltage.

This logic probe is based on CMOS integrated circuits, and is consequently only fully compatible with circuits that are based on 4000 series CMOS devices. In practice it will operate quite well with many TTL circuits, but it can not be guaranteed to do so. It is the higher speeds of TTL circuits rather than differences in logic 0/1 levels that are most likely to cause problems. Rather than taking the risk of getting misleading results by using this unit on TTL circuits, it would be better to build a separate TTL compatible probe. A suitable design is featured as the next project in this book. Both the logic probes are so cheap that building both of them should not "break the bank"!

The Circuit

Figure 3.4 shows the full circuit diagram for the CMOS logic probe. IC1 is used at the front end of the circuit, and this is two gates from a 4001BE quad 2 input NOR gate. The inputs of the two unused gates are tied to the positive supply rail in order to prevent spurious operations and to avoid any risk of damage by static charges. The two gates that are used are connected to operate as simple inverting buffer stages.

IC1a acts as a buffer at the input of the unit, and its input is normally connected to the 0 volt rail by R1. CMOS inputs should not be left floating, and it is therefore important to have this resistor to hold the input at a valid logic level (and provide static protection) under standby conditions. NOR gates are often connected as inverters by connecting both their inputs together, which is the method that has been adopted with IC1b. For IC1a the alternative of taking one input low and using the other as the input of the inverter has been used. This has the advantage of loading the test point by a single CMOS input rather than by two inputs. Fan-out is not usually a problem with CMOS logic devices, where it is usually possible for a single output to drive fifty or more inputs. However, as with any test equipment that taps-off some signal from the circuit under test, loading is something which must always be borne in mind. D1 switches on when the input is low (logic 0), and D2 switches on when the input is high (logic 1).

Pulse detection is provided by IC2, which is a CMOS 4047BE monostable/astable. In this case it is connected in the positive triggered monostable mode. In this application it does not really matter whether the unit is triggered on positive going or negative going edges, since any input pulse will have both types of transition and will trigger the circuit. IC2 is used in the non-retriggerable mode, and this is an important factor. With a retriggerable monostable, holding the input at the appropriate logic level has the effect of extending the

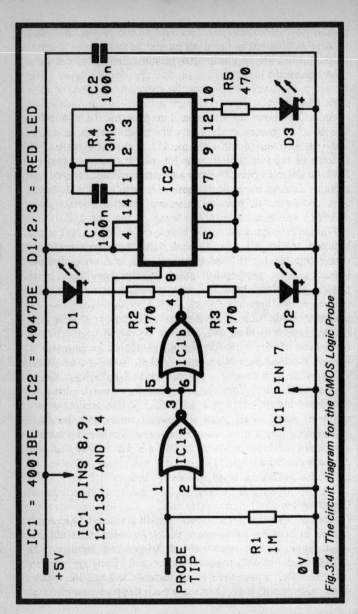

Fig.3.4   The circuit diagram for the CMOS Logic Probe

IC1 = 4001BE   IC2 = 4047BE   D1,2,3 = RED LED

IC1 PINS 8, 9,
12, 13, AND 14

96

output pulse indefinitely. This could obviously give confusing results, with a static input giving the impression that input pulses are present. A non-retriggerable monostable can only be triggered by a transition of the appropriate type. The output pulse always ends after the appropriate period of time regardless of what logic level is present at its input during that time. Once the output pulse has finished, only another transition of the correct type will trigger the circuit again. This ensures that l.e.d. indicator D3 is only triggered when there is an input pulse. C1 and R4 set the flash duration for D3, and the specific values give a duration of very roughly one second. If a shorter flash is preferred, simply make R4 lower in value (the output pulse duration is proportional to the value of this component).

The unit is powered from the circuit under test, and a second crocodile clip lead is included to permit the +5 volt line to be "tapped". The unit could be powered from an internal battery supply, but I would advise against this. Apart from the battery adding bulk and weight to the unit, you should remember that not all CMOS logic circuits operate from a standard 5 volt supply. Most do, but there are plenty of CMOS circuits operating at various supply voltages from 3 to about 15 volts. The probe will not function properly if there is a mismatch in the supply voltages, and there would be a slight risk of the probe being damaged when testing circuits with a supply voltage of more than 5 volts. Powering the unit from the circuit under test is an easy way of avoiding any supply mismatch problems. Of course, the unit under test must be capable of providing the extra current, but in most cases it should be well able to do so. From a 5 volt supply the unit draws only about 4 milliamps with one l.e.d. activated, or about double this with two l.e.d.s switched on

Construction

Figure 3.5 shows the stripboard layout for the CMOS logic probe. It is based on a board having 26 holes by 16 copper strips. There is little out of the ordinary about construction of the board, but both integrated circuits are CMOS types, and they therefore require the standard anti-static handling precautions. One input of IC2 lacks any built-in protection circuits,

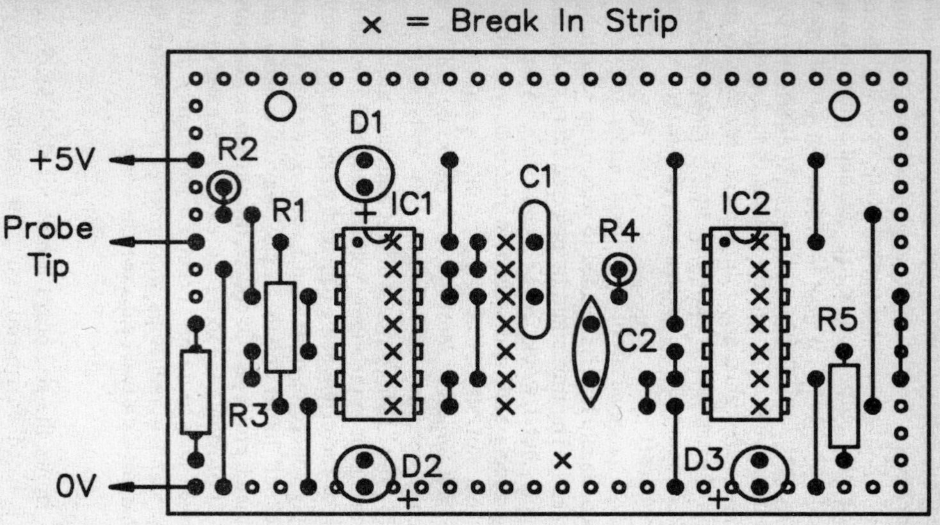

x = Break In Strip

+5V

Probe
Tip

0V

Fig.3.5 The CMOS Probe stripboard layout

98

and I would recommend that the handling precautions are scrupulously observed with this component, even if you do not normally bother too much about them.

Although D1, D2, and D3 are shown as being mounted on the board in Figure 3.5, it is of course quite in order to mount them off-board in panel holders if preferred. I would strongly urge the use of high brightness l.e.d.s, since the l.e.d. current is quite low when the unit is used with low voltage supplies of around 5 volts. You may like to use l.e.d.s of different colours so that the display is easily interpreted even when just quickly glancing at it. The method of denoting the cathode (+) leadout of l.e.d.s varies, but by far the most popular method is to have the cathode lead shorter than the anode one. Also, the cathode leadout is usually much thicker than the anode one close to the body of the component. If necessary you can use trial and error to find the right method of connection. Connecting a l.e.d. the wrong way round should not result in any damage to the component.

Components for Figure 3.4

Resistors (all 0.25 watt 5%)
R1	1M
R2	470
R3	470
R4	3M3
R5	470

Capacitors
C1	100n polyester (C280)
C2	100n ceramic

Semiconductors
IC1	4001BE
IC2	4047BE
D1	Red l.e.d.
D2	Red l.e.d.
D3	Red l.e.d.

Miscellaneous
Small case
Stripboard having 26 holes by 16 copper strips
Two 14 pin DIL holders
Two crocodile clips
Wire, solder, etc.

In Use

The first step when using the unit is to connect the two power supply leads. It is not usually too difficult to find suitable connection points on the circuit under test. If necessary, a couple of short (non-insulated) leads can be soldered to the circuit board of the unit being tested so as to provide suitable take-off points. Be very careful to get the supply leads round the right way. It is a good idea to use red and black leads so that it is very obvious as to which lead is which.

Very often you will notice D3 flash when the probe tip is connected to a test point, and when it is removed again. This is due to an input transition as the probe is connected and disconnected, and does not necessarily indicate a pulse at the test point. In order to be sure that the test point is pulsing you must wait until the end of any initial flash from D3, and any subsequent flash from D3 should be a valid indication. However, be careful to hold the probe tip firmly on the test points. Bad or intermittent connections are almost certain to generate spurious input pulses.

The table on page 101 summarises the l.e.d. states for various types of input signal.

TTL Probe

The circuit diagram for the TTL logic probe appears in Figure 3.6. This is not an exact equivalent to the CMOS version, as it has a rather different input section based on inverters rather than NOR gates. It is essentially the same though, with D1, D2, and D3 providing the same functions as their counterparts in the CMOS probe circuit. The monostable is based on a 74121 (IC2), and use is made of the internal timing resistor. Consequently, if you wish to shorten

Input Signal	D1	D2	D3
Standby	ON	OFF	OFF
Static Low	ON	OFF	OFF
Static High	OFF	ON	OFF
Pulsing (around 1 : 1 mark-space ratio)	ON (dim)	ON (dim)	ON
Pulsing (high mark-space ratio)	OFF	ON	ON
Pulsing (low mark-space ratio)	ON	OFF	ON
Pulsing (low frequency)	FLASH	FLASH	FLASH
Illegal Input Voltage	ON (dim)	ON (dim)	OFF

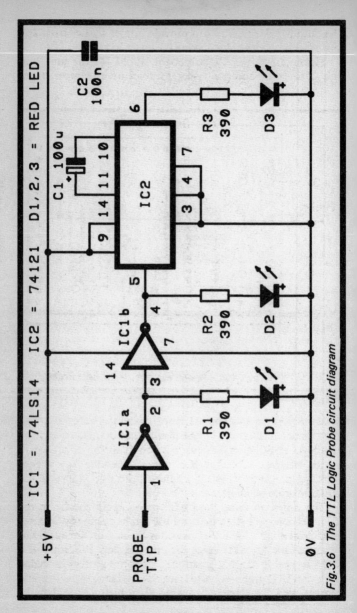

Fig.3.6 The TTL Logic Probe circuit diagram

102

the output pulse duration to provide briefer flashes from D3, this must be achieved by making C1 lower in value.

Figure 3.7 shows the stripboard layout for the unit, and this is based on a board having 23 holes by 16 copper strips.

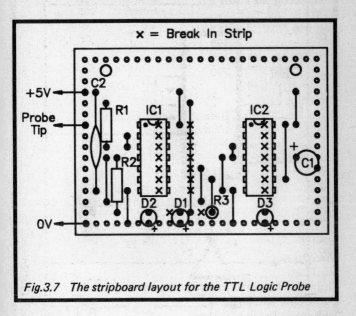

Fig.3.7   The stripboard layout for the TTL Logic Probe

Construction of the board is very straightforward, although the compactness of the layout means that extra care must be taken to avoid short circuits between copper strips due to solder splashes. Neither IC1 nor IC2 require any special handling precautions, but it would still be a good idea to use sockets for these components.

The notes on using the CMOS probe apply equally to the TTL version, and the points on use made previously will not be repeated here. The unit provides loading on the test point equal to one LS TTL input (or one standard TTL input if a 7414 is used in the IC1 position). No input resistor is needed with the TTL probe as there is no risk of damage due to static charges, and the input will always float high. Note that the unit differs in this respect from the CMOS version, where the input is taken low under standby conditions.

Components for Figure 3.6

Resistors (all 0.25 watt 5%)
R1	390
R2	390
R3	390

Capacitors
| C1 | 100μ 10V radial elect |
| C2 | 100n ceramic |

Semiconductors
IC1	74LS14
IC2	74121
D1	Red l.e.d.
D2	Red l.e.d.
D3	Red l.e.d.

Miscellaneous
Small case
Stripboard having 23 holes by 16 copper strips
Two 14 pin DIL holders
Two crocodile clips
Wire, solder, etc.